HELP ME UNDERSTAN
MOBY DICK!

INCLUDES SUMMARY OF BOOK AND ABRIDGED BOOK

HERMAN MELVILLE /
SCOTT LA COUNTE (EDITOR)

SwipeSpeare

ANAHEIM, CALIFORNIA

www.SwipeSpeare.com

Table of Contents

Historical Context

Herman Melville was born on August 1, 1819 in New York City, into a large family. Although he studied surveying at Landingsburgh Academy, he ended up signing on as a cabin boy on the St. Lawrence, which sailed to Liverpool. This was the first of several voyages he served on in his life, including on a whaling ship.

In 1841, when aboard the St. Lawrence, Melville had already begun writing. In 1846, he published Typee, his first book, which was supposedly based on his true experiences. Later, he wrote Omoo, Mardi, Redburn, White-Jacket, Moby Dick, Pierre, and the Confidence Man. Although Moby Dick later came to be known as one of the greatest novel in American literary history, it was not well received at the time of its publication. A final novel, Billy Budd, was published many years after his death.

Since Melville served on a whaling ship, he was more than aware of the dangers and adventures of hunting whales in the mid-1800's. Whale oil was a valuable commodity, and sailors would risk their lives for the fortune the sperm of a great whale like Moby Dick could provide. One could say that any adventure on sea was risky, and hunting an animal that could sink a ship was even more so. But money was not the only reason a man would take to sea, despite the dangers involved.

In the days of Melville, exploring the oceans promised adventure and excitement, as well as an escape from the pressures of society. On a whaling ship, there were no rich or poor, no old or young, no Christian or pagan. Everyone worked under the captain and officers as a single crew, a solidarity that would provide a sense of family for the sailors, as well as help keep them all alive. This desire for adventure and belonging is reflected in Moby Dick, as the main character, Ishmael, seeks a three year voyage on a whaling ship, just to pass the time and get away from the normalcy of life on land.

In light of this historical context, Melville wrote in a way that as much helped the reader imagine being in a whaling crew as enjoy and be entertained by the narrative. Melville juggles the first-person story-telling of Ishmael with the third-person action sequences, which read almost like the stage commands of a play. Packed in between the story, Melville gives a textbook's worth of information about whaling: the working of the ship and boats, the structure of the crew, the process of hunting and catching a whale, how the whale is processed after being killed, and the anatomy of a Sperm whale. For the modern reader, these escapades into educational interludes may be irritating most of the time, but, for the reader of Melville's day, these info-dumps may have been fascinating glimpses into the every-day life of a sailor.

Despite the fact that the book may be difficult for the modern reader, Moby Dick has stood the test of time, enduring as a classic example of masterful storytelling and mid-nineteenth-century artistic style.

PLOT OVERVIEW

The story of Moby Dick centers on Ishmael, who is itching to go out to sea again. He has sailed before on merchant ships, but this time he plans to go to the island of Nantucket and sign on with a whaling ship. He first arrives in New Bedford and stays at a local inn, and it is in this inn that he finds Queequeg, a black man, a cannibal, a harpooneer and whaler. Ishmael and Queequeg seem to clash a bit at first, but they quickly become friends and decide that they will sign on a voyage together.

After a quick ride out to Nantucket and a night's stay in yet another strange inn, Ishmael sets out to find a ship to sign on with. Of the options currently in dock, he chooses the Pequod. He talks to two captains, Peleg and Bildad, both Quaker men but neither the actual captains that will sail with the Pequod. Ishmael manages to get signed on and takes Queequeg back the next day to sign him on, as well. Although the men don't want pagans on board, they are convinced by Queequeg's skill with a harpoon. They sail out early the next morning.

The first several days at sea, the captain, Ahab, doesn't show his face on deck, but he stays locked away in his cabin. When he does reveal himself, he walks with a peg leg, made of whale bone, and carried about a mean temper. He yells at his men, even other sailors, and his mood changes without warning. One day, Ahab collects the crew together to tell them that their mission, other than catch whales and harvest oil, is to find a particular whale, a large, white whale, the one named Moby Dick. Moby Dick is the reason Ahab has a peg leg in the first place. He even nails a gold coin into the mast, saying the gold goes to the first one to spot Moby Dick.

When the crew spots their first whale, boat are lowered to chase it. Everyone is surprised when Ahab himself goes down in his own boat, a boat manned by men the crew had yet to see, special stowaways, one of whom is devilish man named Fedallah. In this encounter, the boat Ishmael is on capsizes, leaving the men to float, hoping for rescue. The Pequod is eventually able to come for them.

As the Pequod moves further south, men begin to see a ghostly spout, blowing mist at night and then disappearing for days at a time. As they go around the Cape of Good Hope, the silvery spout stops appearing.

The first Gam, that is, the first encounter with another ship the Pequod has is with the Goney. Ahab asks about the white whale, hoping the captain of the Goney would know. The other captain is unable to answer well, since his trumpet has blown away in the wind.

The Pequod next crosses paths with the Town-Ho. Ishmael tells the story of the Town-Ho the way it was told to him, of a fight between two officers, one of the officers dying at the end of the story when the ship runs into Moby Dick.

The Pequod sees some strange sighs out at sea. They first run into great meadows of brit, a yellow substance that whales love to eat. Unfortunately, the Pequod is unable to hunt them in the brit. They hear the whales but cannot kill them. Then the crew finds a giant squid, which rises to the surface and sinks down again several times. Some think this is a bad omen, but others, like Queequeg thinks seeing the squid means luck, meaning they'll find a whale soon.

Queequeg's prophecy comes true, and the crew kills a whale. Several chapters are dedicated to the process the crew goes through together when a whale is killed, including fending off sharks, removing the head, and cutting and cooking the oil.

The Pequod next comes into contact with the Jeroboam, a ship that is under control of a madman pretending to be Gabriel the archangel. They also lost a man to Moby Dick. Gabriel warns Ahab that doom with come from anyone hunting the white whale.

The Pequod next kills a right whale, and later another sperm whale. When trying to tap into the great hump on the whales head, an area filled with fat. A man falls in, only to be saved by Queequeg.

The Pequod meets the Virgin, a German ship. They compete for over a whale. The Pequod wins the kill. Later, they come upon a huge school of whales, including mothers nursing their young. Although the men try to capture several, they only kill one.

The next Gam is with the Rose-Bud, a Fench ship. They crew of the Pequod tricks the captain of the Rose-Bud into giving them a whale that is filled with ambergris, a substance that is more valuable than normal oil.

The story takes a turn when the crew comes across the Samuel Enderby, a whaling ship from England. The captain of this ship has lost an arm to Moby Dick, just as Ahab lost a leg. The captain warns Ahab to give up and not chase the white whale. Ahab refuses to listen.

Preparing for his fateful encounter with Moby Dick, Ahab has the ship blacksmith fashion a special harpoon for him, one that must be perfect, one that, once lodged in a whale, would never let go. He even has the weapon tempered with the blood of the three harpooners of the ship.

The Pequod Meets the Bachelor, a happy ship, full of oil. After, they kill four whales at once, having to take a lot of time to process them all. The crew is then hit by a great storm. In the middle of which, Ahab is given the choice to go home and save his crew or risk death and keep hunting Moby Dick. They continue.

After the storm, they mee the Rachel. The captain of the Rachel begs Ahab to help him look for his son, who is lost on a boat in the ocean. Ahab refuses, so he can keep searching to the white whale, who is closer than ever.

They meet the Delight, a ship that was recently attacked by Moby Dick. Once again, Ahab is warned about the futility of trying to kill the white whale. They continue. Soon, they spot the white whale themselves.

After three days of chasing Moby Dick, Ahab is killed and the Pequod is sunk. The only survivor is Ishmael, who is later found by the Rachel, still looking for their lost son, now finding a different orphan.

THEMES

The Whale is Great and Mighty without Equal

The viewpoint character of the novel, Ishmael, has an almost religious reverence for whales, especially for the sperm whale. In fact, Ishmael dedicates so many chapters to praising the greatness of different aspects of the whale, that the reader is likely tired of the subject by the end of the book. Ishmael discusses everything, for the size of the whale to its color, from the strength of its tail to the power of its spout, from its precious fat to the sweet smell of it ambergris. By extension, Ishmael praises the vocation of whaling, since only the greatest of heroes could hope to slay such a magnificent beast. He even searches through the myths and legends of many cultures, finding great heroes of history that may have been whalers. He also degrades the artists that aren't able to draw whales properly, as if they were the makers of false idols. He even sees whales as creatures that are becoming greater with time, pointing to evidence that they are larger now than in times past.

The Whale as Something Mysterious and Indefinable

Adding reason for Ishmael to glorify the great and mighty whale, he also sees them as creatures that are beyond definition or complete understanding. He points to artists' inability to correctly portray the form of a whale. He discusses the thick layer of fat as a means to hid the true person of a whale. Ishmael sees these beasts as creatures of the deep, constantly hidden from sight. Even something as simple as the whale's spout becomes a mystery in Ishmael's eyes, since men don't know what the mist that comes forth from the spout is. That mist is cluttered with superstitions and myths, though Ishmael thinks it is simply water from the sea. By making whales, especially sperm whales, and especially Moby Dick, as abstract as possibly, Melville is able to add terror and anticipation about the Pequod's eventual encounter with the great white whale.

Death

Death is a constant symbol in this novel. From the very start, in one of the beginning chapters, Ishmael goes to a chapel for sailors, and, on the walls, he sees plaques remembering those that have been lost at sea. Every whale the men kill brings death to the front again. The looming danger of meeting Moby Dick grows throughout the book, as the crew learns of more and more people that have been killed by that whale. When Queequeg gets terribly ill, they make a coffin for him, and, when he recovers, he keeps the coffin as a storage chest. When the men finish with a whale, they release the body to float away and get eaten by sharks, a unceremonious ceremony on man calls a funeral. Ahab has dreams about hearses, which he thinks means Moby Dick will die. But it really shows the captain himself will die. The boat is seen as a kind of transition, a voyage, not across the sea, but from life to death. In the end, Ishmael is the only one that escapes death.

The Clash of the Civilized and the Uncivilized

From the start of the novel, there is the struggle when Christianity and civilization meet with savagery and paganism. Ishmael and Queequeg make for strange bedfellows, but they become close friends. When the captains of the Pequod refuse Queequeg because he is not Christian, Ishmael stands up for him, although, in the end, it is Queequeg's skill with the harpoon that convinces them to let him stay. The crew, supposedly Christian men, remain thoroughly superstitious.

The very conflict between proper and wild is seen in man's hunting of the wild whale. No matter how sophisticated the sailors and officers are, carefully mapping out where the whales should be, they still struggle to find one.

The greatest conflict between civilized and savage is within Captain Ahab himself. At times he is kind and compassionate, a wise seaman that can handle man situations. He knows what direction to follow, even when the compass says otherwise. He then makes a new needle for the compass to prove that the old one was broken. He is the man that carefully calculates where Moby Dick will likely be on his map. At the same time, this same man is often the mean-spirited old man that is insane and obsessed with finding the white whale.

The Relationship Ahab has with Moby Dick

Ahab seems to have a strong connection with Moby Dick throughout the novel, even though Moby Dick does not appear in the narrative until the last chapters. From the start, Ahab is visually entangled with whales in that whale done is part of him, serving as his new leg. Ahab's obsession for the white whale is undoubtedly insane. Whenever the Pequod comes across another ship, Ahab does little more than ask about Moby Dick. It seems he cares for little else. The Pequod even does little whaling, since their main mission is to find Ahab's enemy. Ahab's end is fitting, bound to the whale forever by harpoon and rope.

CHARACTERS

Major Characters

Ishmael

Ishmael is the main character of the story of Moby Dick, as well as the viewpoint character. He is characterized as a normal sailor, an everyman. He doesn't play much of a role in the progression of the story, especially after the first few chapters, but he important because he is the observer of all the conflict around him. Ishmael does have one personality trait that taints the entire novel: his love and respect for the might sperm whale. He spends great time in the book trying to communicate the greatness and majesty and mystery of the whale, as well as the majesty of the whalers to pursue these amazing beasts. Ishmael also has the only personal relationship of the novel: a close friendship with Queequeg, savage harpooneer that also comes to serve on the Pequod.

Queequeg

Queequeg is a pagan harpooneer, a one-time savage cannibal that now sails in the western world. Ishmael meets him at an inn in New Bedford. They soon become close friends, so close that they vow they will sail together on the same whaling vessel. Queequeg is only accepted on the Pequod for his amazing abilities as a harpooneer. Throughout the book, Queequeg is seen as something as a superhuman. Twice, he specifically save some from death, once on a small ship, when someone falls overboard, and once when a whaler falls into the forehead of a dead whale, literally drowning in oil. Queequeg even saves himself from death, as he miraculously recovers from a horrible sickness.

Ahab

Ahab is the acting captain of the Pequod. In the first chapters of the book, he is absent, and even when the Pequod is out to sea, he doesn't show his face for some time. Ahab is nearly sixty years old, a man that has spent nearly all of his adult life on the sea. He is married and has a son, but he's spent hardly any time with any of them. Throughout the novel, Melville portrays Ahab as the struggle between two characters: the insane old man, driven by hat and vengeance, obsessed with hunting and killing the white whale, and the experienced and wise old sailor who shows compassion and calm, even in trying situations.

Starbuck

Starbuck is the first mate of the Pequod, a native of Nantucket. He is very thin, but he's also strong. He is highlighted in the novel as the only officer who repeatedly and openly opposes Ahab. They have a series of conflicts throughout the story, culminating when the captain points a musket at the officer. Later, Starbuck finds himself in a position to kill Ahab, but his pity won't allow him to do so. Even when Starbuck knows that taking certain actions will lead to sure doom, he loyally follows orders.

Stubb

Stubb is the second mate of the Pequod, a man from Cape Cod. Stubb has the most amusing personality of all those on board, since Melville writes him with a happy-go-lucky attitude, a man that seems not to have any worries at all. The way Stubb orders his men, and the way he cheers them on as they row toward a whale, is highlighted several times for its unique combination of urgency and lackadaisicalness.

Fedallah

One more especially noteworthy character is Fedallah, a man of uncertain Asiatic origins. This is the man that Ahab smuggles on board, along with a crew of rowers, for the captain's personal whaling boat. Fedallah is seen as a mysterious and sinister person. Some among the crew think him to be a demon or the devil himself. They speculate that Ahab has sold his soul to Fedallah in order to catch the white whale. At one point, Fedallah does seem to prophecy, making a vow that Ahab will survive his encounter with Moby Dick. He makes Ahab believe he is immortal. It is ironic, therefore, that Fedallah dies the day before Ahab, both at the doing of Moby Dick.

Minor Characters

Flask

Flask is the third mate of the Pequod. He plays a very little role in the story of the novel. He is described as the lowest of the officers, which means he is treated in such a way that he wishes he were among the ordinary men of the ship.

Pippin

Pippin, of Pip, is a young black man who is assigned as oarsman for one of the boats. His fear gets the best of him, though, and he twice jumps from the boat to avoid confronting a whale. In the end, he goes mad.

Tashego and Dagoo

Tashtego and Dagoo are the two other harpooners that serve on the Pequod. Tashtego is an Indian from Martha's Vineyard, and Dagoo is a huge African man.

Dough-Boy

Dough-Boy is the ship's steward, the one who serves the officers their dinner.

SUMMARY OF CHAPTERS

Before Chapter 1 (Part One): Etymology

Before we can get to the famous opening lines of Moby Dick, Melville takes us on a linguistic and historical safari to get a more rounded background of whales. The first part, and etymology of whale, is supposedly written by an Usher to a Grammar School, as he ever dusts his old lexicons and grammars. He gives several dictionaries' opinions about the origin of the word whale, as well as a long list of the translation for whale in several languages, both current and dead.

Before Chapter 1 (Part Two): Extracts

The second pre-chapter-one introduction to Moby Dick is a list of extracts of quotes referring to whales. The collector of these clippings is a sub-sub-librarian, referred to simply as the Sub-Sub, a lowly person Melville looks down upon and pities. The extract come from the bible (references to the Leviathan, especially), historical documents, memoirs and journals, poetry, and Shakespeare, and scores of other sources from across history and around the globe. The reader must work his way through page after page of these extracts before finally reaching the first chapter, perhaps wondering if Melville is trying to work up drama or simply play some kind of practical joke. The extracts do, however, highlight the massiveness of whales, and perhaps such descriptions (such as a dead whale being confused for a small island, a whaling ship hiding behind it) of size and danger are meant to tease the reader's imagination.

Chapter 1: Loomings

"Call me Ishmael," the opening words to Moby Dick, set the scene and introduce the protagonist, who will also be the viewpoint character. Ishmael describes his reasons for wanting to go out to sea by saying that, simply, he has nothing particular to interest him on shore. He explains that, whenever he wants to see the 'watery part of the world,' he does so as a sailor, and not as a passenger, an obvious choice for someone that isn't independently wealthy. He has apparently gone out to sea before, but always of merchant ships. This will be the first time he goes on a whaling ship, and this fact makes him very excited, an excitement for seeing firsthand the hunting and killing of such a giant and mysterious animal.

Chapter 2: The Carpet-Bag

Ishmael packs his carpet-bag and prepares to head out to sea. He travels to New Bedford, which is a port town, but his final destination is Nantucket. He explains that, while so many young men may prefer New Bedford, he will only settle for sailing aboard a Nantucket craft. But because Ishmael must stay in New Bedford for some days before going on to Nantucket, he decides to look for a place to stay, finally settling on a place called "The Spouter Inn: Peter Coffin."

Chapter 3: The Spouter-Inn

Melville/Ishmael describes the Spouter Inn (since the point of view is played with from the beginning), a smoky, older place filled with people. He pays close attention to a painting on the wall, blackened with smoke, most of its contents hard to identify. Ishmael does figure the object in the middle in a great whale in an ocean. Ishmael is told that there aren't any beds available, but he can share beds with a harpooneer. Ishmael at first objects, but, after considering the cold night outside and the likelihood of finding another place to stay, he decides he'll take his chances with the harpooneer. A bit indecisive, Ishmael later changes his mind again, thinking he'd rather sleep on a bench in the dining area. The innkeeper tells him how the harpooneer is out "peddling heads," that is, selling shrunken heads from some islands he'd recently sailed by. Then, as the harpooneer hadn't come back to the inn for hours now, Ishmael changes his mind again and decides to go sleep in the room. While he's trying to get some sleep, he's shocked to find the harpooneer arrive, a savage man with tattoos and a tomahawk-shaped pipe for smoking. After rough introductions, Ishmael and Queequeg, the harpooneer, settle down and get some sleep.

Chapter 4: The Counterpane

Ishmael wakes up with Queegueg's arm wrapped around him as if they were lovers. He feels trapped in this situation, and remembers how, as a child, he was once punished to stay in bed for most of a day, almost unable to bear counting those hours. He finally manages to wake the savage man, and Queegeug rises and dresses and goes outside, leaving Ishmael in peace to also get dressed for breakfast.

Chapter 5: Breakfast

Ishmael joins the group of renters downstairs for breakfast, which is served at a great table. These men, sailors all, are surprisingly quiet while eating. Ishmael eats and observed the men. Queegueg is at the head of the table, using his harpoon to bring food closer to himself. He eats nothing but steaks cooked rare--yet another peculiarity that makes Ishmael wonder how civilized this cannibal is.

Chapter 6: The Street

After breakfast, Ishmael goes out for a walk in New Bedford, which he described for the reader. This town has the strange and international feel of a port town, with more savages and merchants walking the streets. Most interesting here is Ishmael's description of the differences between a city-person and one from the country, the latter being considered more dainty than the first. Country boys come to make a name for themselves in the whaling business, only to appear comical in their choice of clothes.

Chapter 7: The Chapel

Ishmael sets out to find a Whaleman's chapel nearby. He enters to find the place quiet, with people walking about. Queequeg, surprisingly sits there, as well. All around, Ishmael sees plaques with names of people inscribed on them, along with how each person died: lost at sea, fallen overboard during a storm, hauled off by a great whale. The chaplain has not yet arrived, and Ishmael reflects on the fact that he may, too, die at sea this voyage, but he is ready for whatever fate.

Chapter 8: The Pulpit

While Ishmael is seated in the chapel, Father Mapple comes in, a one-time harpooneer and sailor, now a minister. He walks to the front of the chapel, where the pulpit is. Ishmael takes some time to wonder over the pulpit, since it has some strange characteristics. First, it is taller than the rest of the room, something normal for most churches. But this pulpit is so high, one wouldn't be able to climb onto it easily, there are no stairs. Instead, there is a rope latter, like one from a ship, which Father Mapple uses to climb onto the pulpit, after which he pulls the latter up, as if the pulpit were a ship setting out to sea.

Chapter 9: The Sermon

Throughout Father Mapple's sermon, there is something strange about how he speaks: he addresses the church like sailors, calling himself a captain of the church, referring to all in attendance as shipmates. The content of the sermon is fitting, a story from the bible about a voyage in open waters, when Jonah tried to run from God's assignment for him. Father Mapple tells things that aren't exactly in the bible, like how and why the captain would have allowed Jonah on his ship in the first place, drawing lessons for the "shipmates" at church to learn from. At the end of the sermon, the Father dramatically concludes and covers his face, kneeling silently until everyone has left the church.

Chapter 10: A Bosom Friend

Ishmael and Queequeg become close friends. Ishmael arrives back in the Inn from church, Queequeg already there, having come back early from the sermon. Ishmael finds the savage counting pages in a large book. Though he can only count to fifty, it seems, Queequeg understands and is amazed at the number of pages by the number of times he gets to fifty and has to start counting again from zero. Ishmael approaches him, and they establish that they should continue to share a bed and become friends. Queequeg likes the idea, and, after supper, he asks Ishmael to share with him in his nightly idol worship. Ishmael reluctantly agrees, and they go to bed together, bosom buddies.

Chapter 11: Nightgown

Ishmael and Queequeg, in bed together, are unable to sleep. They talk and nap at intervals, but eventually, all sleep leaves them, and they sit up in bed. Queequeg begins to tell his story, a story Ishmael is eager to hear.

Chapter 12: Biographical

Queequeg tells of his savage origins. He grew up on an island called Rokovoko, a prince among his people. Queequeg had a great desire to see the western, Christian world, but his father, the High Chief, forbid it. Against his father's wishes, Queequeg requested a job as sailor on the next boat that passed by the island, the boat stopping by for supplies. The captain of the boat said no, but Queequeg was determined. As the boat was leaving, he paddled alongside it in his canoe and climbed aboard. When the captain found him, he reluctantly allowed him stay. Since then, Queequeg has worked as a sailor and harpooneer. Ishmael and Queequeg agree to try to sail together on the next voyage.

Chapter 13: Wheelbarrow

Ishmael and Queequeg head out to take a ship to Nantucket. They use a wheelbarrow to carry all their things, and Queequeg tells a story about the first time he used a wheelbarrow, not knowing what it was, carrying it on his back while everyone laughed at him. Queequeg also tells about when a westerner came to his tribe and confused the drinking bowl for a wash bowl and plunged his hands into it, to the whole tribe's astonishment. They get on the Moss, a ship. On board, someone makes fun of Queequeg, and the savage threatens him. While the captain is reproving Queequeg, a man falls overboard. In an instant, Queequeg is the one that jumps in a save the man, later being voted a hero by all on deck.

Chapter 14: Nantucket

Ishmael take time to describe the island of Nantucket, a one-time home to red-skinned Indians, now a place where some of the greatest whaling ships dock between voyages.

Chapter 15: Chowder

The two arrive in Nantucket and go to an inn called Try Pots, a place referred to them by their previous host, a place owned and run by the Husseys. Mrs. Hussey takes them in to eat, and asks if they want clam or cod. Ishmael doesn't understand, decides on the clam, but still can't imagine how one clam can feed a fellow for the nigh. They are surprised to receive a lovely supper of clam chowder, a meal that Mrs. Hussy is famous for. Unfortunately, Queequeg is not allowed to take his harpoon upstairs with him, for safety.

Chapter 16: The Ship

That night, Queequeg tells Ishmael that his little idol has insisted that Ishmael go alone to find a ship that both of them would work on. Ishmael is reluctant at first, but, the next morning, he does head out in search of a ship. He finds three in bock: the DEVIL-DAM, the TIT-BIT, and the PEQUOD. Ishmael decides on the last of those three, and boards to investigate. There, he sees a tent right on the deck of the ship, and out from the tent, he meets both Captain Peleg and Captain Bildad, neither of which being the Captain of the Pequod. Ishmael signs on with the ship, and leaves to tell Queequeg the good news.

Chapter 17: The Ramadan

While Ishmael is looking for a ship to sign on with, Queequeg is using the day for his Ramadan, or fasting and humiliation. Ishmael stays away from the inn for the most part of the day. When Ishmael finally does return to the room he shares with the savage, upon knocking, nobody answers. Again and again Ishmael calls, but there is no answer. Calling Mrs. Hussey, Ishmael demands an ax, in order to break the door down. At last, they get the door open, only to find Queequeg sitting on the floor, unmoving. Despite everything Ishmael does, Queequeg doesn't make a move until first light of the following morning. The two of them then get ready to go to the ship, the Pequod.

Chapter 18: His Mark

When the two arrive at the ship, there is problem. The two captains, both Quakers, won't allow any savage to board. They claim Queequeg must show papers that he is a Christian. Ishmael argues the Queequeg is as much a Christian as anyone, since he belongs to the universal church of mankind. What really persuades the captains, though, is the savage's ability with the harpoon. Queequeg manages to strike a small tar stain on the floor, no bigger than a whale's eye. With haste, the captains sign Queequeg on as harpooneer, giving him a much better pay grade than they'd given Ishmael.

Chapter 19: The Prophet

As the two friends leave the ship, both having signed now, they meet a strange man, who claims to be a prophet. This man claims they will be in grave danger while sailing on the Pequod. He calls Captain Ahab, who Ishmael has yet to meet, Old Thunder, and speaks of some event in the recent past that has changed Ahab into a crazy man. Ishmael makes little of this man's words, but only asks his name, which is Elijah.

Chapter 20: All Astir

Ishmael and Queequeg are called to help in the loading of the boat, the move their stuff on board and work with the crew. Ishmael keeps asking about the captain, Ahab, but has yet to meet him. They are told that the next day they are sure to sail, so they get some sleep and get ready for an early start.

Chapter 21: Going Aboard

Ishmael and Queequeg are up and ready to board at six the next morning, but they find no one on dock in this half-darkness. Ishmael does see some figures climb onto the ship, though he can't see who they are. They are surprised from behind by Elijah, the old "prophet." He asks if they're going aboard, and he also asks if they saw someone board. Ishmael, surprised by the question, says yes. But when they make it to the ship, there isn't anyone but one sleeping man below deck. Where did the ghostly figures go?

Chapter 22: Merry Christmas

The Pequod ships out, with captains Bildad and Peleg running things. No one has seen Ahab, yet, who is apparently staying in his cabin. They give orders left and write, in their peculiar Quaker way of talking. Finally, they leave the ship, hopping over to another boat, and bid the crew farewell and good luck.

Chapter 23: The Lee Shore

Ishmael recognizes one of the crew as a person he'd met in the inn. Ishmael is amazed that man, Bulkington, is ship out again, so soon after the last time he sailed. Ishmael praises him in his thoughts for being such a tough sailor and brave man.

Chapter 24: The Advocate

Ishmael reminisces about the fame and dangers of whaling. Many do not, concludes Ishmael, truly appreciate the honor of being a whaler. He talks a little about whaling through history, and address such questions as: is whaling honorable, profitable, good or bad, respectable, and so forth.

Chapter 25: Postscript

Coming of his thought from the preceding chapter, Ishmael continues to think about the importance of whaling. He concludes that, since royalty is crowned by pouring oil on the head, and since that oil must be whale oil, a king or queen is crowned with the fruits of a whaler's labors.

Chapter 26: Knights and Squires

Ishmael now begins to describe some of the men that serve on the Pequod, starting with the chief mate, Starbuck, a thin but strong man born in Nantucket.

Chapter 27: Knights and Squires

Ishmael continues to describe Stubb, the second mate. Stubb is from Cape Cod, a man that is continually smoking a pipe, of which is has many stored away in his quarters. The third mate, Flask, is from Martha's Vineyard. Each mate also has a harpooneer assigned to him. Starbuck has Queequeg as his harpoon man. Tashtego, an Indian, is with Stubb, and Dagoo, a negro-savage, stays with Flask. When a whale is seen, these three mate would each take a boat and harpooneer to chase and kill the beast.

Chapter 28: Ahab

For days after setting into sea, Ishmael sees nothing of Captain Ahab. The official story is he's gotten sick, and he's simply waiting for better weather to leave his cabin. When he does appear, Ishmael sees him for the first time. The most notable thing about Ahab is his peg leg, which appears to be carved from whale bone. He is also rumored to have a scare the stretches from his head to his toes, a scar that he got from a "force of nature."

Chapter 29: Enter Ahab; to Him, Stubb

Stubb and Ahab have a conflict over nothing at all. Ahab calls Stubb a dog and threatens to beat him. No one knows why Ahabs is so grumpy.

Chapter 30: The Pipe

Stubb, still obviously upset about his run-in with the captain, throws his pipe into the ocean.

Chapter 31: Queen Mab

Stubb and Flask and talking on deck. Stubb talks about a strange dream he had the night before, in which Ahab was kicking him with his peg leg, as if Stubb were a dog. The dream seems to take a turn, as Stubb is kicking a pyramid, and Ahab calls him wise. Suddenly, Stubb woke up in his hammock. Flask suggests that Stubb not talk to Ahab anymore, as long as it's possible to avoid him. There, on the deck, is Ahab, telling the men to keep their eyes peeled for a white whale. Upon hearing this, both Stubb and Flask are convinced that the captain's crazy.

Chapter 32: Cetology

Ishmael shares a form of Cetology with the reader, that is, a system to classify whales into easy-to-understand groups. First, he defends the idea that whales are fish, although he admits there are certain key differences (the horizontal tail fins, for example). He then lays out a classification system that includes several different kinds of whales. The three major divisions are Folio Whale, Octavo Whale, and the Duodecimo Whale, all three of which are named after book types. Each division is further divided into books and chapters, branching out into a full classification system.

Chapter 33: The Specksnyder

Ishmael talks about the history of the harpooneer in whaling ships. Apparently, the harpooners were at one time the head members of the ship. There was a Chief Harpooneer that was equal to the captain. The captain was in charge of navigation and the daily routines of the ship, but when a whale was spotted, the harpooners took control. Through time, though, and as whaling spread to other countries, the position of the harpooners changed. Now, in American Nantucket ships, the harpooners are in no way considered officers, but they retain certain privileges. For example, they have better lodging within the ship, and they eat in the captain's cabin.

Chapter 34: The Cabin-Table

The insane ritual of eating a meal for the officers is explained. Whenever Dough-Boy, the steward announced that dinner is ready in the cabin, Ahab enters first. When Starbuck is sure that Ahab has settled down at the table, he enters the cabin. Mr. Stubb goes in next, but only when he believes Starbuck is seated. Finally, Flask, when he thinks everyone has already found their seat, enters the cabin. Flask, as the lowest of the officers, is in the worst situation, since not only does he have to sit down last, but he must leave the cabin first. There are days the Flask eats very little because, when he's barely begun his meal, the others are ready to leave.

Chapter 35: The Mast-Head

The Mast-Head is the look-out place on the main mast of a ship. Ishmael describes how whaling ships keep mean up there all the time to spot whales in the distance. More luxurious ships have crow's nests, complete with benches for comfort. But the whaling ship has little more than a place to stand. Ishmael says that, when he is assigned to the mast-head, he never sees a whale, because he is too much a thinker. Alone with the wind and open sea, he gets so lost in thought that he forgets to look for surfacing whales. He does mention that he isn't as bad as others, who, in their thoughts and daydreams, might step right off the plank and fall to their deaths.

Chapter 36: The Quarter-Deck

Captain Ahab assembles the entire crew to the deck. He tells them about a white whale, and instructs them to yell out as soon as they spot it. Some of the men recognize the mention of a white whale as the legendary Moby Dick, with a curious spot and slanted brow. Ahab offers a gold coin for the first man to spot this whale. It also comes to light that this Moby Dick is also the whale that is responsible for Ahab's missing leg. Starbuck, however, is not happy about this. Ahab says they will chase Moby Dick around the world if need be, but Starbuck thinks hunting for vengeance over hunting for profit is wrong.

Chapter 37: Sunset

Ahab, watching the sunset, thinks about his mission to find the white whale. He knows some of his crew think him mad, but he also knows they are right, and in the lust for the chase, he is captive for but one destiny.

Chapter 38: Dusk

Starbuck is on deck, leaning against the mainmast. He reflects, grudgingly, on his situation. He also detests the kind of crew he is stuck with, group of drunks and wild men.

Chapter 39: First Night Watch

Stubb laughs at Starbuck's earlier quarrel with Ahab.

Chapter 40: Midnight, Forecastle

The harpooners and sailors are in the forecastle, having something of a party, singing and drinking together. They speak of life on the sea and of women. Most importantly, they all seem very excited to be on this mission with Ahab to hunt the white whale. Their wild chat is interrupted by a squall, which is a sudden storm.

Chapter 41: Moby Dick

Ishmael has also gotten caught up in the craze of hunting the White Whale, Moby Dick. He reflects of the numerous run-ins with Moby Dick, and at the ominous reputation the whale has earned. He is described not only as unusually large and dangerous, but also as ghostly, almost supernatural. His body is full of marks and scars from whaling ships trying to catch him, but always the result is disastrous. This chapter gives us a feeling of coming danger, from the way Ishmael describes Ahab's nemesis.

Chapter 42: The Whiteness of the Whale

Ishmael further tries to describe Moby Dick through his white color, a hue not common among whales. He admits that some things are made more beautiful in white, like a white pearls, but he chooses to focus more on the otherworldly and terrorizing aspects of white. He give examples like the white bear of the north pole, an unusually large and vicious bear. He also talks of the white shark of the tropics (which we know as the "great white," something especially terrifying after the movie Jaws) and the giant white bird, the albatross. He also mentions albinos, which are feared and hated in many cultures, and the pale white tint of a dead person. Focusing on Moby Dick's white color, instead of giving an idea of purity or beauty, in Ishmael's eyes, gives even more terror to the whale.

Chapter 43: Hark!

Members of the crew are passing buckets to each other. They hear a noise below deck, and rumors abound about something mysterious and unknown being on board.

Chapter 44: The Chart

Captain Ahab is not worried about not being able to find Moby Dick in the great oceans of the world. He has kept a detailed chart of white whale spottings, and has calculated where it will be by following the drifting food of the giant creature. He plans to intercept the monster and kill it. He has dreadful dreams of Moby Dick, and, when he awakens, he is deeply disturbed by those dreams. While certainly obsessed, we can see in this chapter that the captain is not all crazy, but he is a smart, calculating sea man who is intelligently hunting his quarry.

Chapter 45: The Affidavit

Ishmael shares some information he has about whales and whale encounters. First, there have been occasions in which a whale, after being harpooned, escapes. Also, he knows of times when a whale seems to somehow enjoy being hunted. There are many stories of whales as huge and unbeatable creatures, but Ishmael sees such stories as exaggerations of the truth. He does admit, though, that a sperm whale of great size can, when angered, destroy a ship. It has happened on several historical voyages. So, while the stories are exaggerated, Ishmael reminds us, and perhaps reminds himself, that there is real danger in whaling, especially in hunting a giant sperm whale with a history of violence toward men.

Chapter 46: Surmises

Ahab, though obsessed with finding and killing Moby Dick, also realizes that he can't neglect his duty as captain, and that means not forgetting the main purpose of the voyage. He knows that he has control over Starbuck, at least for now, but he may lose that power if he single-mindedly hunts one whale, when the crew is expecting to hunt many whales. While the crew is excited about their mission, they also have financial needs back home, meaning it is in their best interest to collect the oil from any whale they see. Ahab tries to find a balance between his consuming desire to find Moby Dick and his rational nature as an experienced captain.

Chapter 47: The Mat-Maker

Ishmael and Queequeg are weaving a sword-mat as part of their boat. While weaving, Ishmael is reminded of the weave of destiny in the Loom of Time. They are interrupted by Tashtego, who yells, "there he blows," meaning a whale has been spotted! Ahab orders the men to their boats, and they are lowered down to the sea. Everyone is surprised that Captain Ahab boards his own boat, with a team that no one has met before. These were the shady phantoms Ishmael had seen the first morning he boarded the Pequod.

Chapter 48: The First Lowering

The boats move out to capture the whale. Unfortunately, it is not Moby Dick. With the whale submerged, they must follow a slight disturbance in the water, and a little mist, to predict where the whale will come up. Stubb gives orders to his men in a strange way, both with seriousness and as a joke. Finally, Queequeg is able to get a harpoon shot at the whale, a strike that isn't enough to kill it, and it gets away. The boat Ishmael and Queequeg are in is toppled over, and the men nearly drown before the main ship can come and rescue them.

Chapter 49: The Hyena

Ishmael imagines that the universe must be laughing at them, that they are the victims of some kind of grand joke. He feels this way when he faces extreme tribulation. He asks Stubb if it was wise to go after the whale under those circumstances, and he asks Queequeg is such near-death experiences are common on whale voyages. He doesn't like the answer to either. He decides to make a will for himself, in case he should die on this voyage, and he has Queequeg come down and be his lawyer and witness.

Chapter 50: Ahab's Boat and Crew. Fedallah

Stubb and Flask talk about the surprising boat and crew of Captain Ahab. Stubb finds this interesting, considering that Ahab has only one leg. Also, this stowaway crew of men is a grand surprise. Fedallah is described as a strange and quiet men or unknown Asiatic origin.

Chapter 51: The Spirit-Spout

The Pequod sails easy for several weeks, and the crew grows accustomed to the new members of the crew, those men that rode out with Ahab to catch a whale. The one that seems strange, however, is Fedallah, who move in almost a phantom way and has some kind of power or influence over Ahab. South of St. Helena, Fedallah spots a silvery spout. Ahab commands the ship to give chase. After some days, the spout is seen again, appearing and appearing at night, but then staying out of sight for days at a time. Finally, the spout is lost, and the ship makes it to the Cape of Good Hope. Ahab's strange actions in this chapter show how he is still tormented by his drive to find Moby Dick.

Chapter 52: The Albatross

The Pequod comes across another ship on the open ocean, her name being Goney (or Albatross). The ship is described as being bleached white like bones. When the two ships, the Pequod and the Goney, get close, Ahab yells out about the white whale, trying to zero in on Moby Dick's location. The captain of the Goney tries to communicate back, but little is heard from him because the wind carried away his trumpet. In frustration, Ahab gets no more information. This chapter show the Pequod as isolated and lonely, and perhaps not even one step closer to catching the white whale.

Chapter 53: The Gam

Gam is a word not used by anyone else but sailors, and so Ishmael sees fit to describe what it is now. A Gam is when two ships meet on the ocean. The captains meet and talk, and the crew engages in social visits. Ahab chooses not to go on the Goney because of the threat of storm on the in the wind and waves. This is most strange, since whalers have much reason to be social with other ships, even exchanging letters and information. For Ahab, however, a Gam would be a waste of time if it won't lead him to Moby Dick, so the two ships go their separate ways.

Chapter 54: The Town-Ho's Story

Ishmael tells the story of the Town-Ho, a ship the Pequod next meets on the waters. The Town-Ho was struck by three tragedies that almost destroyed it. First, it was hit by a sword fish and started taking on water. Second, a struggle between two officers causes a near-mutiny, tearing the crew of the ship apart. In the heat of this conflict, mostly between the principle players, Steelkilt and Radney, Moby Dick attacks the ship. Radney is crushed in Moby Dick's jaws and dies. This chapter shows two things. First, Ishmael is recording the story not as a sailor on the Pequod, but as a survivor of the Pequod's journey, telling it to others in an inn some time later. This means Ishmael will survive the voyage, though it isn't certain who else does. Second, the story gives Moby Dick teeth, as it were, by showing how deadly he can be.

Chapter 55: Of The Monstrous Pictures of Whales

In this chapter, Ishmael seems very concerned about pictures of whales throughout history, eager to dispel misconceptions these images may have created. He begins with the earliest pictures of whales, from Hindu, Egyptian, and Grecian sources, explaining the different errors made, whether it was a mistake of anatomy or a misclassification. While trying to explain whales in a more exact and informative way, Ishmael actually makes whales seem more mysterious and indefinable creatures, aliens of the deep. Saying that one artist's depiction of a sperm whale looks more like a squash than the actual creature, Ishmael shows what little man knows about the leviathan. Looking at the skeleton of a whale would help little, according to him, since that central structure bears little resemblance to a fleshed out whale at sea.

Chapter 56: Of the Less Erroneous Pictures of Whales, and the True Pictures of Whaling Scenes

Here, Ishmael continues the discussion from the previous chapter, about pictures of whales, allowing that there are few visual depictions that are more or less accurate. Ishmael talks about four published outlines of Sperm Whales that he knows of, outlines he sees as not too bad, insisting that Beale is the best, since all his drawings are acceptable except for one.

Chapter 57: Of Whales in Paint; In Teeth; in Wood; in Sheet-iron; in Stone; in Mountains; in Stars

What connects all cultures and civilizations of the world; what one thing runs through all of them, like one bright thread running through a dull fabric? Ishmael argue that it is, in fact, the whale. He points to artistic interpretations of the whale from around the world and throughout history. This, of course, makes the voyage of the Pequod one of universal proportions, one of all men against one great beast.

Chapter 58: Brit

The Pequod comes upon a great expanse of brit, a yellow substance that serves as food for the Right Whale. Feasting within this golden meadow are many of such whales, but, as long as they remain in the brit, they are safe from the whalers' attack. The crew can but wait, hearing the cheerful whales in the distance. Here, too, Ishmael fills in even more details about the whaling industry.

Chapter 59: Squid

A white mass is spotted in the distance, and one of the crew cry out that Moby Dick is nearby. This causes the crew to explode into action, lowering boats, harpoons ready and eager. But the great white mass they find turns out to be something other than Moby Dick. It is a mysterious giant squid, which keeps rising to the surface and then dropping into the deep again. This is said to be an ominous sign, since few crews see a giant squid and live to tell the tale.

Chapter 60: The Line

Since it will be important in future chapters, Ishmael takes some time to describe the whale-line, which is the special kind of rope that whalers attach to their harpoons. It is very strong, but it's also soft and flexible, more so than normal line that is used on the ship. When a whale is harpooned, this line is deadly dangerous for all men on the boat, since getting caught in it can harm or kill a man. Ishmael uses this line as a metaphor to describe the dangers of life all around us, the mortality we all must face.

Chapter 61: Stubb Kills a Whale

While everyone is absolutely worried about seeing the squid, since it is supposedly a bad omen, Queequeg has a different take on the situation. When a squid is seen, he insists, a whale is sure to follow. And that is exactly what happens. Ishmael spots a large sperm whale rolling in the water, almost playing. Stubb and his men go after it in the boat and harpoon it. The whale continues to roll and eventually dies.

Chapter 62: The Dart

Here, Ishmael stops the narrative to add detail to one thing that was present in the previous chapter: the dart. He describes the dangers and difficulties of coming up on a whale in a boat, and the process he harpooneer goes through the kill it.

Chapter 63: The Crotch

Ishmael also describes the crotch, which is basically a wooden stick that comes out of the boat, shaped and positioned in such a way that the harpoon can be leaned against it, ready for a quick grab and throw.

Chapter 64: Stubb's Supper

The boats struggle to bring Stubb's kill up to the ship, a task that takes a long time, since the whale carcass won't budge. They cut a steak from the whale and cook it. Stubb, not happy with the steak, feeling it's overcooked, talks to the cook, Fleece. He asks Fleece where he thinks he'll go when he dies, and Fleece answers he'll go to heaven. Stubb isn't so sure about this, and a religious conversation ensues.

Chapter 65: The Whale as a Dish

Ishmael gives us a history of the whale's tongue and how it was a delicacy in many cultures. He seems to exhault the whale, showing it to be useful for much more than only oil. Especially among the whalers themselves is whale a much envied meat, a noble dish indeed.

Chapter 66: The Shark Massacre

The dead whale is brought up alongside the ship, but it is late at night, so the cutting and cooking of the whale's fat will have to wait for morning. A major reason why the job cannot be done at night is the danger of sharks. Masses of sharks attack at the whale. Queequeg nearly looses a hand while trying to fend them off. In this chapter, Ishmael also gives more information about the whaling process itself.

Chapter 67: Cutting In

The men, specifically Stubb and Starbuck, cut a hole in the whale, so they can put a hook in a hoist some of the whale's mass up to deck level. The ship is nearly sunk in the process. This chapter highlights the massiveness of the whale's body, the sheer size of the creature. One might wonder what a living whale could do to the Pequod.

Chapter 68: The Blanket

Ishmael describes the amazing massiveness of the whale as it is hoisted up. The whale is covered in a thick layer of fat, which Ishmael fixates on throughout the chapter, comparing this skin and fat to a blanket or a poncho, something that covers and protects the animal, something that also disguises it and give it mass and form. Here, we get the feeling that there is something hidden about the whale, something we cannot completely understand because it is buried beneath unimaginable amounts of blubber. So the whale, even when hoisted out of the sea, even when studied from up close, continues to be something somewhat mysterious and difficult to define.

Chapter 69: The Funeral

The whale is now beheaded, and the cutting is done. The body of the whale, a giant white mass, since, even after all that cutting, the overall size of the animal hasn't change very much, floats away, sharks picking off chunks. This process is called a mocking funeral by one of the crew. The theme of dead and danger is made obvious here, except now the roles are reversed: instead of the ship risking danger with the whale, the whale is "buried" by the ship.

Chapter 70: The Sphynx

Ishmael gives details to the beheading of a whale and the hoisting of the whale head up out of the water. Only skilled whale surgeons pride themselves with the ability to cut off the head, since, for one thing, whales don't have anything that resembles a neck, and, secondly, the beheading must be done from the deck, ten feet above the whale, with a long cutting instrument. The whale head is hoisted up, and Ahab speaks to it as if it could speak back, asking what sights the great beast has seen. This shows, perhaps, Ahab's great respect for whales, treading them as persons. But, more likely, this shows his insanity and dementia. Either way, the head obviously remains silent, unable to give Ahab the information he seeks.

Chapter 71: The Jeroboam's Story

The Pequod crosses paths with another Nantucket ship, the Jeroboam. The crew has been infected with some kind of epidemic, so the captain doesn't get close to the Pequod. Alos, one member of the Jeroboam's crew who is a Shaker prophet, now claiming to be Gabriel the Archangel, literally taking control of the ship, playing upon the superstitions of the crew to make himself greater than the captain. Ahab wants to know from the captain of the Jeroboam if they've seen the white whale. The captain has, and one of his crew was killed by the run in with Moby Dick. Gabriel warns Ahab and the Pequod's crew that calamity comes to anyone that seeks the white whale, using the unfortunate end of the "blasphemer" as an omen.

Chapter 72: The Monkey-Rope

Ishmael continues his description of the cutting process whalers must do to their kill. Often the harpooneer has to stay on the whale's body throughout the process. Queequeg is there, and Ishmael holds him there with a rope while the others work. Ishmael compares the rope and Queequeg to a monkey on a leash, dancing around his owner. We see the close relationship between Ishmael and Queequeg highlighted in this chapter, as well as even more details of the whaling process.

Chapter 73: Stubb and Flask Kill a Right Whale; and Then Have a Talk over Him

The Pequod's mission is to focus on sperm whales, and the captain's personal mission is to capture Moby Dick, a very special sperm whale. However, when evidence points to many Right Whales in the area, Ahab orders that a right whale by killed. Stubb and Flask do just that, and they wonder why the captain would allow the taking of such an inferior whale. Meanwhile, the two men wonder about Fedallah. They believe him to be the devil, with his tail curled up out of sight. Perhaps Ahab has sold his soul to Fedallah for the chance to capture Moby Dick, or perhaps Fedallah is planning to kidnap Ahab.

Chapter 74: The Sperm Whale's Head Contrasted View

Ishmael praises the Sperm Whale, showing how is superior to the right whale. The Sperm Whale has a massive head, but it's eyes and ears are tiny by such standards. Ishmael finds it amazing that the creature can perceive the world in such a way.

Chapter 75: The Right Whale's Head Contrasted View

The right whale has an insignificant head compared the strong head of the sperm whale. It is compared to a shoe. It has little oil, no valuable ivory bones, and so is nothing compared to a sperm whale.

Chapter 76: The Battering Ram

This chapter describes how a battle between a giant sperm whale, like Moby Dick, and a whaling vessel, like the Pequod, would play out. Ishmael talks about the forehead of the sperm whale, which is a giant mass, rising vertically from the water like a cliff, free of tenderness or vital organs, meaning the head would serve as a perfect battering ram, able to destroy a ship.

Chapter 77: The Great Heidelburgh Tun

Ishmael describes the upper cranium of the sperm whale, an area that can be called the Heidelburgh Tun. Below that, there is a great reserve of oil. This whopping amount of sperm makes the whale so valuable. Ishmael is describing all this to prepare us for future chapters, in which we'll see the draining of a whale's sperm.

Chapter 78: Cistern and Buckets

We can but imagine how dangerous a confrontation with a living whale can be, and what's been described so far shows us some of the perils whalers face. This chapter shows the dangerous lives of whalers, dangers that prevail even after the whale is dead. While the crew is trying to tap into the Tun and get to the oil, Tashtego falls into the opening to the head, disappearing into the sperm. He is thought to be lost, but Queequeg, thinking quickly, is about to save him. He dives to the side of the whale's head, cuts a small opening in the skin, digs around and pulls Tashtego out head first. Ishmael compares this saving of the crew member to the birth of a child, Tashtego escaping from the womb of sperm, born again into the world of the living, Queequeg serving as deliverer.

Chapter 79: The Prairie

Ishmael describes the face of the whale, highlighting that it doesn't have a nose, except, of course, for the blow hole on the top of its head. Again, the sperm whale is seem as mysterious and difficult to define. This anomalous creature, with a full front that is clean and sublime, showing what Ishmael calls genius. But the whale doesn't have to prove itself to anyone or offer its features for interpretation. Instead, its pyramidical silence speaks for itself, as a monument to its own greatness, a design that defies nature, almost as if it were as artificially made as the actual pyramids.

Chapter 80: The Nut

Everything about the great sperm whale is massive and powerful--everything, that is, except for its brain. Ishmael allows that the brain is small, unusually so for the size of its body. He claims the lack of size in the brain is made up for, however, by the great size of the spinal cord.

Chapter 81: The Pequod Meets the Virgin

The Pequod meets a ship called Virgin, a ship whose captain begs for some oil from Ahab. Ahab, of course, is only interested in one thing: the white whale. The captain of the Virgin claims he knows nothing about this Moby Dick. Ahab gives him some oil, and the ships separate. When a whale is spotted, though, the two ships find themselves competing for the kill. Ahab's boats get the better of the German boats and they make the kill. The whale, once dead, starts to sink, which is strange, since sperm whales usually float when they are dead. Ahab shows patriotism as he sends out his boats, sure of the superiority of American whalers over German ones.

Chapter 82: The Honor and Glory of Whaling

Ishmael has such a personal investment in the pride of whaling, he is now showing mythological references to whales. He wants the readers to think that Perseus, Vishnoo, and St. George were all whalers, even implying that the "dragon" Saint George killed was really a great whale. This makes the quest for a whale a more universal and mythic story, the crew of the Pequod like heroes in a legend.

Chapter 83: Jonah Historically Regarded

The sailors of the Pequod have problems believing the biblical story of Jonah, since certain details don't match with what they've seen of life on the sea and whales. This is the second time Jonah is discussed directly in the novel, and this time from a completely different perspective. Now, just as Ahab battles insanity and experienced seamanship, just as Ishmael can't decide if he's amazed and mystified by the great whales or absolutely scared by them, logic and science butt heads against mythology and religion. One large objection to the story of Jonah has to do with the digestive juices of the whale, which would kill Jonah in much less than three days. Ishmael, however, responds that the whale could very well have been dead. Also, the geography doesn't seem to match reality, since no whale could travel so far in three days, and since Nineveh is more than three days walk from the shore. Ishmael dismisses such doubts and tries to explain them.

Chapter 84: Pitchpoling

Queequeg anoints any boat he uses, something he superstitiously believes will make it faster. Ishmael also describes yet another aspect of whaling: something he calls pitchpoling, which is when a lance is thrown from a rocking boat.

Chapter 85: The Fountain

In this chapter, Ishmael focuses on yet another aspect of the whale's anatomy: the spout. The spout is important for the whaler, since a whale can only be spotted and hunted when it comes up for air, which is less often that one might think. The mist that seems to come from the whale's spout is something of a mystery, and Ishmael talks about different ideas as to what it is and does. Some think it is powerful, poisonous, or even blinding, perhaps some substance that originates from deep within the whale itself. Ishmael, however, dismisses such ideas, guessing that the mist is simply that: mist from the sea, perhaps from water that the whale ingested while feeding.

Chapter 86: The Tail

Here, Ishmael shows again his great respect, almost a reverence, for the giant sperm whales of the world, focusing, in this chapter, on just one aspect of the whale's anatomy: the tail. He talks about the parts of the tail, details of how it looks and works, and the different ways the tail is used by the whale, which vary from playing, "kitten-like," in the sea to using it to fight other whales or whaling ships. Ishmael's fear of the mighty tail makes it difficult for him to describe. This chapter also shows the way whalers view the whale, not only as prey to hunt and kill, but also as a deadly hunter of the sea.

Chapter 87: The Grand Armada

Now sailing in the Indian Ocean, the Pequod happens upon a large group of whales, described as a Grand Armada. The boats race to maim as many of the whales as possible, using ball-and-chain type tools called druggs. While hunting and maiming, the crew notices the whales that stay just under the surface of the water: nursing mothers with their babies. The men are mesmerized by this sight. In the end, they only manage to capture one of the whales of the group.

Chapter 88: Schools and Schoolmasters

Ishmael takes time to describe groups of whales, called schools. In a school of female whales and children, there is usually one large and young male that leads them. The male, then, is called the schoolmaster. There can also by schools of males, and this kind is much more dangerous to encounter, for obvious reasons. An interesting difference Ishmael notices is that female-only schools stay together when attacked, but male-only groups may spread out, each whale for himself. This is a difference in sexes that Ishmael sees among humans, too. In this chapter, by comparing whales to humans and finding some qualities that seem consistent between man and whale, he seems to give soul to the whale, making Moby Dick, their eventual prey, more like a person than a simple animal.

Chapter 89: Fast-Fish and Loose Fish

Taking a look at one aspect of whaling from a legal point of view, Ishmael describes the difference between a fast-fish and a loose-fish. This comes up when more than one whaling ship is hunting the same animal. What is one boat harpoons the whale, but another boat succeeds in killing the beast? Ishmael cites a rule of thumb that can help. A fast-fish is a whale that is fastened or connected by a manned vessel, therefore making it owned by that boat or ship. No other captain can claim the whale when it is a fast-fish. But, even if one boat harpoons a whale, if the animal is loose, it is free game. Ishmael goes on to compare this distinction to human rights, saying they are like a loose-fish, difficult to secure or claim and always disputable.

Chapter 90: Heads or Tails

Ishmael goes on to talk about property and legal standards of whaling, focusing now on an unusual custom in some lands. When whalers capture a whale, they may be required to present the head to the king and the tail to the queen. Ishmael has no idea why this is so, or why the queen would want the tail of a whale. But the unfortunate truth of this requirement is that whales are basically nothing by a head and a tail, meaning the poor whalers are left with next to nothing to keep for themselves.

Chapter 91: The Pequod Meets the Rose-Bud

The Pequod comes upon a French ship called the Rose Bud, a whaling ship that currently has two whales tied to it. Ahab, of course, interested in only one thing, asks about the white whale, about Moby Dick. The captain of the Rose-Bud has not even heard of the whale. Stubb notices, though, that one of the whales tied to the Rose-Bud has ambergris, and he tricks the captain into leaving the whale behind so they can steal it. He tells the captain of the Rose-Bud that there is a problem with the whales they've captured and that they should just leave them be and go lest they ruin their ship. The captain believes Stubb and leaves the whales, allowing the Pequod to take the whale for itself.

Chapter 92: Ambergris

As we should be used to by now, Ishmael stops the narrative to explain something which he believes will help us appreciate what's happening in the story. In this case, he describes what ambergris is and why it's so valuable to whalers. This substance is a fine delicacy that can sell for a high price back home. This gives reason for Stubb's behavior in the last chapter. Ishmael also addresses a myth about whales, something that often reflects poorly on the whole whaling profession: the idea that all whales always stink. Ishmael argues that the oil, and especially ambergris, of a whale is sweet smelling. He says that whales are healthy creatures, since they are always bathing (in water) and getting exercise and eating healthy.

Chapter 93: The Castaway

This chapter focuses on one member of the crew: Pip. Pip is a ship-keeper, which means he remains on the ship when the others go out on the boats to hunt a whale. But, during the processing of the whale with ambergris, when one of Stubb's oarsmen sprains his hand, Pip is assigned to the boat to take his place. When boats are lowered to catch a whale, Pip is so afraid that he jumps from the boat, getting tangled in a rope. Stubb decides to cut the rope to save Pip's life, but says the boy must not be afraid the next time. Pip jumps again later, still a coward, and, to avoid punishment, ends up getting picked up by another ship. Pip ends up away from the Pequod, having realized that the crew would be willing to sacrifice him in order to catch a whale. This of course is only a sample of the insanity Ahab has; while Stubb would sacrifice one life to accomplish his mission as a whaler, Ahab would sacrifice the entire crew to catch Moby Dick.

Chapter 94: A Squeeze of the Hand

The crew works together to squeeze the sperm for Stubb's whale. While describing this part of the whaling process, the preparing of the sperm, Ishmael describes his feelings as an "abounding, affectionate, friendly, loving feeling." Whether from the sense of community he feels working with the crew, a satisfaction of reaping the bounty of a kill, the pleasantness of the sperm itself, or some combination of all three, Ishmael certainly enjoys this squeezing process.

Chapter 95: The Cassock

Queequeg is doing an interesting job. Suspended on a wooden horse, he cuts pieces of the whale's blubber for storage below. Ishmael juxtaposes Christianity and pagan idolatry with vivid symbolism.

Chapter 96: The Try-Works

Ishmael describes to the reader an interesting part of American whaling ships: the Try-Works. Ishmael is manning the try-works when he realizes that he has turned himself around. He fixes the problem just in time to stop the ship from capsizing. This shows the constant danger the sailors face as sea.

Chapter 97: The Lamp

In previous voyages, Ishmael was always on merchant vessels, on which oil was a scarce commodity. That meant getting dressed and doing other chores in the dark most of the time, since lamps were rarely lit. On a whaling ship, especially one that has met with great success in the hunt, there is such a superabundance of oil that lamps can be lit at any time and for any reason. Because of this luxury, there is actually a lamp that stays lit almost all the time.

Chapter 98: Stowing Down and Clearing Up

This chapter continues to describe the process of preparing and storing the sperm oil of a whale. The sperm is stored in barrels, and, when cooled, it's later put into flasks below deck. Interestingly, the oil has a fine cleansing quality, leaving the deck cleaner and whiter than before, clearing away any sign of blood or gore.

Chapter 99: The Doubloon

While walking about on the deck of his ship, Ahab keeps going back and looking at one object: a gold doubloon. After giving careful study of the coin, he decides it must be from Ecuador. Starbuck is observing the captain, and think him to be egotistical. Studying the inscriptions on the coin, the symbols it contains, Ahab judges that the white whale will be caught in a month and a day.

Chapter 100: Leg and Arm. The Pequod, of Nantucket, Meets the Samuel Enderby, of London

The Pequod crosses paths with yet another ship, the Samuel Enderby, an English ship. The captain has a arm of whale bone, just as Ahab has his leg. Ahab asks if they have seen the white whale, only to discover that Moby Dick is the one that took the captain's arm off. The doctor of the English ship talks of the horrible wound the captain sustained, warning Ahab to steer clear of the white whale. When Ahab refuses to listen, the English captain wonders if he is crazy.

Chapter 101: The Decanter

Ishmael gives more details about the English ship that the Pequod encountered in the previous chapter. The Samuel Enderby is named after a great merchant in London. He talks about the gam between the two ships, which included a fine meal. Ishmael praises the generosity of the Englishmen.

Chapter 102: A Bower in the Arsacides

Ishmael gives details about the internal construction of the sperm whale. He tells of Tranquo, king of the Tranque, one of the Arsacides, who found the bones of a whale and brought it from shore, making a temple out of the remains. This little story gives more merit to the major theme of whales and religion.

Chapter 103: Measurement of the Whale's Skeleton

Ishmael gives details about the size of a whale, as well as its weight. The details are not exactly important, but one thing that stands out here is the fact that Ishmael sees a whale as a fit match for a ship, meaning a conflict could be deadly for the crew. Ishmael even compares the bones and ribs of a whale to the hull of a great ship.

Chapter 104: The Fossil Whale

Ishmael continues to marvel at the great size and strength of the sperm whale. He thinks about writers who inflate the subjects of their books, while Ishmael finds himself dumbstruck when thinking about how fit such a great beast into a volume of any size.

Chapter 105: Does the Whale's Magnitude Diminish? Will He Perish?

Ishmael wonders is whales of today are in any way smaller than the ones of ancient times. He decides that, if anything, whales are larger now than before. He cites specific whale bones that have been found and historic references to the sizes of whales. Ishmael feels the species of the sperm whale to be immortal.

Chapter 106: Ahab's Leg

Ishmael focuses on the agony Ahab suffers because of Moby Dick, discussing some of the discomforts he goes through because of his leg. The captain has at times fallen or stumbled because of the peg leg.

Chapter 107: The Carpenter

Ishmael describes the carpenter aboard the Pequod, not physically, but as the kind of man he is. Ishmael finds him unique and remarkable.

Chapter 108: Ahab and the Carpenter

Ahab visits the carpenter about fixing his leg. We see the relationship the men have, a fascinating one indeed. It seems that, while Ahab rules over the rest of the crew like a grouchy and insane tyrant, the carpenter and the captain seem to be on more or less equal footing.

Chapter 109: Ahab and Starbuck in the Cabin

Starbuck discovers the there is a leak in the containers and they are losing oil. He tells the captain that they must doing something about it, since they could easily lose as much oil in another day than they could make in a year. Ahab dismisses the advice, saying they should allow the casks leak because he, Ahab, too is leaking. Starbuck gets angry, only to find a musket in his face, Ahab's finger on the trigger. In the conversation that ensues, Ahab eventually takes Starbuck's advice.

Chapter 110: Queequeg in his Coffin

Queequeg gets sick, and, due to the severity of his fever, everyone expects that he will die. A coffin is even made for him, at Queequeg's insistence. As time passes, though, he recovers, claiming that a man can stare a sickness down and decide to live, healing himself through pure willpower. Recovered, Queequeg keeps the coffin and uses to store his things. He even carves the tattoos that he sports on his body onto the lid of the coffin.

Chapter 111: The Pacific

The Pequod makes it to the Pacific Ocean, and Ishmael is excited to be there. Ahab, on the other hand, is thinking only of his adversary, Moby Dick.

Chapter 112: The Blacksmith

Ahab has the blacksmith work on his leg to make it fit better to the captain's body and form. We learn a bit about the blacksmith, a man that lost everything on land and chose to go to sea instead of commit suicide.

Chapter 113: The Forge

Ahab talks more to the blacksmith. He wants the man to make him a harpoon of superior quality, something that would stick into a whale and never let go. After several tries, all of which Ahab reject for imperfections, the blacksmith succeeds in making a wonderfully wicked harpoon. Ahab has the weapon tempered with the blood of the three harpooners, pagan all, Queequeg, Tashtego, and Daggoo.

Chapter 114: The Gilder

Having reached a special hunting area close to Japan, the crew goes out on boats to search for whales. Things seem pleasant and good, and even Ahab's spirits seem lifted.

Chapter 115: The Pequod Meets the Bachelor

The Pequod meets another Nantucket ship, called the Bachelor, a whaling ship that is overly weighed down with oil, after a successful whaling run, the crew celebrating before beginning the long voyage home. Ahab asks about Moby Dick, only to hear that the captain of the Bachelor doesn't believe the white whale even exists.

Chapter 116: The Dying Whale

The Pequod spots four whales and kills them all. Ahab, having stuck a whale himself, watches it die, and reflects on what such death teaches us about mortality.

Chapter 117: The Whale Watch

The killing four whales at the same time is too much for a whaling ship to handle. So men must stay with whales through the night. Ahab stays on the whale's back through the night, with Fedallah. The captain has a dream about hearses, not the first of such dreams that he's woken up from. He tells Fedallah about the dream, and Fedallah swears that the white whale can't kill him, that only the gallows could take his life. Ahab truly believes he is immortal.

Chapter 118: The Quadrant

Ahab calculates the Pequod's position, wondering where his enemy could be now. He looks upon his quadrant, a tool for calculating latitude, and calls it a foolish toy. For Starbuck and Stubb, watching on, Ahab will undoubtedly dies during their struggle with Moby Dick.

Chapter 119: The Candles

The Pequod hits a storm, and her canvas is torn. Fighting through the typhoon, Starbuck sees two options: head back home and to safety or risk death be fighting the winds and looking for Moby Dick. Ahab says he can see lights and lightning that will lead them to the white whale. The officers speak of mutiny, but Ahab insists that they have all taken an oath to find Moby Dick. Therefore, that is what they will do.

Chapter 120: The Deck Towards the End of the First Night Watch

As the storm rages, Starbuck approaches the captain, but Ahab dismisses him.

Chapter 121: Midnight The Forecastle Bulwarks

Stubb and Flask are on the bulwarks, lashing down the anchors. They argue about the possibility that the ship will catch fire in this storm.

Chapter 122: Midnight Aloft Thunder and Lightning

Tashtego is lashing down the mainsail. He questions as to the purpose of thunder, and says that he wants run instead of thunder.

Chapter 123: The Musket

The storm finally calms, early in the morning hours. Starbuck goes into the captain's room to tell him and finds asleep. He also find loaded muskets on their rack. He remember how Ahab almost shot him before, and nearly kills Ahab. But, looking at the old sleeping man, Starbuck can't bring himself to do it and leaves.

Chapter 124: The Needle

Ahab comes out of his cabin the next morning, a quiet day after the storm. He judges that the needle on the compass is wrong, that the storm turned the compass. He has the ship turned around. He officer quietly question Ahab's judgment. Showing himself to still be a wise seaman, Ahab fashions a new needle out of the steel of a lance, proving that he was right when the compass was wrong.

Chapter 125: The Log and Line

Ahab now turns his attention to the log and line, to make sure they are also working properly. Two men are going on about something that Ahab considers foolishness. He asks Pip for help, but the boy has gone crazy and is saying nothing but gibberish. The captain puts him in the cabin to rest, showing compassion to the poor boy.

Chapter 126: The Life-Buoy

Strange things begin to happen on the ship. One sailor claims he is hearing sounds the foretell bad happening. Soon after another sailor falls from the mast and dies. The life-buoy is lost trying to save the sailor from drowning. Queequeg offers his coffin so the carpenter can make a new life-buoy.

Chapter 127: The Deck

Ahab watches the carpenter as he works to turn the coffin into a life-buoy. They have a bit of an argument, sine Ahab sees the entire project as a waste of time. The carpenter manages to keep his cool.

Chapter 128: The Pequod Meets the Rachel

The next ship the Pequod crosses paths with is the Rachel. Ahab discovers he knows the captain of the Rachel, and, even better new for Ahab, they have seen the white whale just a day before. The captain of the Rachel asks Ahab to help him look for a lost whaling boat, since the sailor on it is his son. The captain even tries to appeal to Ahab's heart by saying he knows Ahab has a son, as well. Ahab refuses, saying he can't lose time and must find Moby Dick.

Chapter 129: The Cabin

When Ahab leaves the cabin, he sees Pip is following him up to the deck. Pip is following the captain, and as Ahab tries to lose him, Pip weeps. Ahab eventually threatens to kill the boy, showing he won't do anything or take time for anything when Moby Dick can be so close.

Chapter 130: The Hat

Ahab, desperate to find the whale, asks Starbuck to help him climb up onto the perch. He wants to be the first one to see the white whale. As he searches from the perch, a hawk swoops by and takes his hat. This is a bas omen.

Chapter 131: The Pequod Meets the Delight

The next, and last, ship the Pequod runs into is the Delight, a broken and limping vessel, practically in ruins. Ahab asks if they've seen the white whale, and the captain indicates his ship as proof of a confrontation. The captain of the delight claims no harpoon in the world could stop that monster, but Ahab insists that his harpoon, forged from lightning and blood, will be able to kill the beast. The Pequod moves on.

Chapter 132: The Symphony

Ahab keeps searching for the whale. As Starbuck approaches, they talk about Ahab's first kill, a whale when he was eighteen. He says that since then, he has only spent a total of three years on shore. His wife and son are practically strangers to him, so much so that he calls her a widow. Ahab shows doubt about the futility of his chase. But, still, they move on .

Chapter 133: The Chase First Day

Ahab feels that Moby Dick near before he sees him, and even when visual contact is made, some of the crew don't believe him, until it is confirm by another. The boats are lowered and the chase begins. Ahab chases the whale, and Moby Dick plays with him before sinking his boat. Ahab narrowly escapes onto Stubb's boat. They return to the ship to look for the whale again.

Chapter 134: The Chase Second Day

The second day, Moby Dick is again spotted. The crew works together, and they attack the whale in the boats. But again the whale fights back. They discover that Fedallah has dies, caught in a rope and dragged underwater. Starbuck outwardly criticizes Ahab about allowing his men to die, but when Ahab responds, the crew sides with him.

Chapter 135: The Chase Third Day

The crew attack Moby Dick again, once he is spotted. Ahab's boat is thrown over, and they narrowly escape. Moby Dick rams the Pequod, which begins to sink, sharks waiting in the waters below for fresh meat. In an act of desperation, Ahab harpoons Moby Dick, but is entangled in the ropes and is dragged into the ocean. The ship sinks, taking everyone with it.

Epilogue

The epilogue shows how Ishmael survives. He is in a boat when the Pequod goes down, and he is nearly sucked down with the whirlpool of the sinking ship. Surviving, he is later found by the Rachel, still desperately searching for their lost boat.

The Condensed Moby Dick

ABRIDGED FOR THE MODERN READER

[1]

LOOMINGS

Call me Ishmael.

Some years ago—never mind how long precisely—having little or no money in my purse, and nothing particular to interest me on shore, I thought I would sail about a little and see the watery part of the world. It is a way I have of driving off the spleen and regulating the circulation. Whenever I find myself growing grim about the mouth; whenever it is a damp, drizzly November in my soul; when-ever I find myself involuntarily pausing before coffin warehouses, and bringing up the rear of every funeral I meet; and especially whenever my hypos get such an upper hand of me, that it requires a strong moral principle to prevent me from deliberately stepping into the street, and methodically knocking people's hats off—then, I account it high time to get to sea as soon as I can. This is my substitute for pistol and ball. With a philosophical flourish Cato throws himself upon his sword; I quietly take to the ship. There is nothing surprising in this. If they but knew it, almost all men in their degree, some time or other, cherish very nearly the same feelings towards the ocean with me.

Now, when I say that I am in the habit of going to sea whenever I begin to grow hazy about the eyes, and begin to be over conscious of my lungs, I do not mean to have it inferred that I ever go to sea as a passenger.

No, when I go to sea, I go as a simple sailor, right before the mast, plumb down into the forecastle, aloft there to the royal mast-head. True, they rather order me about some, and make me jump from spar to spar, like a grasshopper in a May meadow. But what of it, if some old hunks of a sea-captain orders me to get a broom and sweep down the decks?

But wherefore it was that after having repeatedly smelt the sea as a merchant sailor, I should now take it into my head to go on a whaling voyage; this the invisible police officer of the Fates, who has the constant surveillance of me, and secretly dogs me, and influences me in some unaccountable way—he can better answer than anyone else. And, doubtless, my going on this whaling voyage, formed part of the grand programme of Providence that was drawn up a long time ago.

I stuffed a shirt or two into my old carpet-bag, tucked it under my arm, and started for Cape Horn and the Pacific. Quitting the good city of old Manhatto, I duly arrived in New Bedford. It was a Saturday night in December. Much was I disappointed upon learning that the little packet for Nantucket had already sailed, and that no way of reaching that place would offer, till the following Monday.

My mind was made up to sail in no other than a Nantucket craft, because there was a fine, boisterous something about everything connected with that famous old island, which amazingly pleased me.

Now having a night, a day, and still another night following before me in New Bedford, ere I could embark for my destined port, it became a matter of concernment where I was to eat and sleep meanwhile. It was a very dubious-looking, nay, a very dark and dismal night, bitingly cold and cheerless. I knew no one in the place.

With halting steps, I paced the streets, and passed the sign of "The Crossed Harpoons"—but it looked too expensive and jolly there. By instinct followed the streets that took me waterward, for there, doubtless, were the cheapest, if not the cheeriest inns.

At last I came to a dim sort of light not far from the docks, and heard a forlorn creaking in the air; and looking up, saw a swinging sign over the door with a white painting upon it, faintly representing a tall straight jet of misty spray, and these words underneath—"The Spouter Inn:—Peter Coffin."

Coffin? —Spouter? — Rather ominous in that particular connection, thought I. But it is a common name in Nantucket, they say, and I suppose this Peter here is an emigrant from there. As the light looked so dim, and the place, for the time, looked quite enough, and the dilapidated little wooden house itself looked as if it might have been carted here from the ruins of some burnt district, and as the swinging sign had a poverty-stricken sort of creak to it, I thought that here was the very spot for cheap lodgings, and the best of pea coffee.

Upon entering the place, I sought the landlord, and telling him I de-sired to be accommodated with a room, received for answer that his house was full—not a bed unoccupied. "But avast," he added, tapping his forehead, "you haint no objections to sharing a harpooner's blanket, have ye? I s'pose you are goin' a-whalin', so you'd better get used to that sort of thing."

I told him that I never liked to sleep two in a bed; that if I should ever do so, it would depend upon who the harpooner might be, and that if he really had no other place for me, and the harpooner was not decidedly objectionable, why rather than wander further about a strange town on so bitter a night, I would put up with the half of any decent man's blanket.

"I thought so. All right; take a seat. Supper? — you want supper? Supper'll be ready directly."

The fare was of the most substantial kind—not only meat and potatoes, but dumplings; good heavens! One young fellow in a green box coat, addressed himself to these dumplings in a most direful manner.

"Landlord," I whispered, "that ain't the harpooner is it?"

"Oh, no," said he, looking a sort of diabolically funny, "the harpooner is a dark complexioned chap. He never eats dumplings, he doesn't — he eats nothing but steaks, and he likes 'em rare."

"The devil he does," says I. "Where is that harpooner? Is he here?"

"He'll be here afore long," was the answer. "But come, it's getting dreadful late, you had better be turning flukes—it's a nice bed.

I considered the matter a moment, and then upstairs we went, and I was ushered into a small room, cold as a clam, and furnished, sure enough, with a prodigious bed, almost big enough indeed for any four harpooners to sleep abreast.

I sat down on the side of the bed, and commenced thinking about this head-peddling harpooner. But beginning to feel very cold now, I made no more ado, but tumbled into bed, and commended myself to the care of heaven. Just then I heard a heavy footfall in the passage, and saw a glimmer of light come into the room from under the door.

Lord save me, thinks I, that must be the harpooner, the infernal head-peddler. But I lay perfectly still, and resolved not to say a word till spoken to. Holding a light in one hand, and that identical New Zealand head in the other, the stranger entered the room, and without looking towards the bed, placed his candle a good way off from me on the floor in one corner, and then began working away at the knotted cords of a large bag. I was all eagerness to see his face, but he kept it averted for some time while employed in unlacing the bag's mouth. This accomplished, however, he turned around—when, good heavens! what a sight! Such a face! It was of a dark, purplish, yellow color, here and there stuck over with large blackish looking squares. Yes, it's just as I thought, he's a terrible bedfellow; he's been in a fight, got dreadfully cut, and here he is, just from the surgeon. But at that moment he chanced to turn his face so towards the light, that I plainly saw they could not be sticking-plasters at all, those black squares on his cheeks. They were stains of some sort or other. him, and demand a satisfactory answer concerning what seemed inexplicable in him.

Meanwhile, he continued the business of undressing, and at last showed his chest and arms. As I live, these covered parts of him were checkered with the same squares as his face; his back, too, was all over the same dark squares; he seemed to have been in a Thirty Years' War, and just escaped from it with a sticking-plaster shirt. Still more, his very legs were marked, as if a parcel of dark green frogs were running up the trunks of young palms. It was now quite plain that he must be some abominable savage or other shipped aboard of a whaleman in the South Seas, and so landed in this Christian country. I quaked to think of it.

The next moment the light was extinguished, and this wild cannibal sprang into bed with me. I sang out, I could not help it now; and giving a sudden grunt of astonishment he began feeling me.

Stammering out something, I knew not what, I rolled away from him against the wall, and then conjured him, whoever or whatever he might be, to keep quiet, and let me get up and light the lamp again. But his guttural responses satisfied me at once that he but ill comprehended my meaning.

"Who-e debel you?"—he at last said—" you no speak-e, dam-me, I kill-e."

"Landlord, for God's sake, Peter Coffin!" shouted I. "Landlord! Watch! Coffin! Angels! save me!"

"Speak-e! tell-ee me who-ee be, or dam-me, I kill-e!" again growled the cannibal, but thank heaven, at that moment the land-lord came into the room light in hand, and leaping from the bed I ran up to him.

"Don't be afraid now," said he, grinning again, "Queequeg here wouldn't harm a hair of your head."

"Stop your grinning," shouted I, "and why didn't you tell me that that infernal harpooner was a cannibal?"

"I thought ye know'd it; but turn flukes again and go to sleep. Queequeg, look here—you sabbee me, I sabbee you—this man sleepe you—you sabbee?"

"Me sabbee plenty"—grunted Queequeg, sitting up in bed.

"You gettee in," he added, motioning to me, and throwing the clothes to one side. He really did this in not only a civil but a really kind and charitable way. I stood looking at him a moment. For all his tattooings he was on the whole a clean, comely looking cannibal. What's all this fuss I have been making about, thought I to myself—the man's a human being just as I am: he has just as much reason to fear me, as I have to be afraid of him. Better sleep with a sober cannibal than a drunken Christian.

"Good night, landlord," said I, "you may go."

I turned in, and never slept better in my life.

Upon waking next morning about daylight, I found Queequeg's arm thrown over me in the most loving and affectionate manner. You had almost thought I had been his wife. At length, Queequeg rose, and commenced dressing at top by donning his beaver hat, a very tall one, by the by, and then—still minus his trousers—he hunted up his boots. What under the heavens he did it for, I cannot tell, but his next movement was to crush himself—boots in hand, and hat on—under the bed; when, from sundry violent gaspings and strainings, I inferred he was hard at work booting himself; though by no law of propriety that I ever heard of, is any man required to be private when putting on his boots.

The rest of his toilet was soon achieved, so I proposed a social smoke; and, producing his pouch and pipe, he quietly offered me a puff. If there yet lurked any ice of indifference towards me in the Pagan's breast, this pleasant, genial smoke we had soon thawed it out, and left us cronies. He seemed to take to me quite as naturally and unbiddenly as I to him; and when our smoke was over, he pressed his forehead against mine, clasped me round the waist, and said that henceforth we were married; meaning, in his country's phrase, that we were bosom friends; he would gladly die for me, if need should be. After supper, and another social chat and smoke, we went to our room together.

There is no place like a bed for confidential disclosures between friends. Man and wife, they say, there open the very bottom of their souls to each other; and some old couples often lie and chat over old times till nearly morning. Thus, then, in our hearts' honeymoon, lay I and Queequeg—a cozy, loving pair.

Next morning, we borrowed a wheelbarrow, and embarking our things, including my own poor carpet-bag, and Queequeg's canvas sack and hammock, away we went down to "the Moss," the little Nantucket packet schooner moored at the wharf.

It was quite late in the evening when the little Moss came snugly to anchor at Nantucket, and Queequeg and I went ashore.

Next day, after a cozy night and overmuch rich chowder at the Try Pots Inn (the finest such establishment on the island, I had confidently been informed); and after much prolonged sauntering and many random inquiries, I learnt that there were three ships up for three-years' voyages—The Devil-dam, the Tit-bit, and the Pequod. DEVIL-DAM, I do not know the origin of; TIT-BIT is obvious; PE-QUOD, you will no doubt remember, was the name of a celebrated tribe of Massachusetts Indians; now extinct as the ancient Medes. I peered and pried about the Devil-dam; from her, hopped over to the Tit-bit; and finally, going on board the Pequod, looked around her for a moment, and then decided that this was the very ship for us, for Queequeg and I had resolved to be ship mates.

You may have seen many a quaint craft in your day, but take my word for it, you never saw such a rare old craft as this same rare old Pequod. She was a ship of the old school, rather small if any-thing; with an old-fashioned claw-footed look about her. Long seasoned and weather-stained in the typhoons and calms of all four oceans, her old hull's complexion was darkened like a French grenadier's, who has alike fought in Egypt and Siberia. Her venerable bows looked bearded. Her masts—cut somewhere on the coast of Japan, where her original ones were lost overboard in a gale —her masts stood stiffly up like the spines of the three old kings of Cologne. Her ancient decks were worn and wrinkled, like the pilgrim-worshipped flag-stone in Canterbury Cathedral where Becket bled. But to all these her old antiquities, were added new and marvelous features, pertaining to the wild business that for more than half a century she had followed. She was a thing of trophies. A cannibal of a craft, tricking herself forth in the chased bones of her enemies. Scorning a turnstile wheel at her reverend helm, she sported there a tiller; and that tiller was in one mass, curiously carved from the long narrow lower jaw of her hereditary foe. A noble craft, but somehow a most melancholy! All noble things are touched with that.

Now when I looked about the quarter-deck, for someone having authority, in order to propose myself as a candidate for the voyage, at first, I saw nobody; but I could not well overlook a strange sort of tent, or rather wigwam, pitched a little behind the main-mast. And half concealed in this queer tenement, I at length found one who by his aspect seemed to have some authority.

"Is this the Captain of the Pequod?" said I, advancing to the door of the tent.

"Supposing it be the captain of the Pequod, what dost thou want of him?" he demanded.

"I was thinking of shipping."

"Thou wast, wast thou? I see thou art no Nantucketer—ever been in a stove boat?"

"No, Sir, I never have."

"Dost know nothing at all about whaling, I dare say—eh?

"Nothing, Sir; but I have no doubt I shall soon learn. I've been several voyages in the merchant service, and I think that—"

"Merchant service be damned. Talk not that lingo to me. Dost see that leg? —I'll take that leg away from thy stern, if ever thou talkest of the merchant service to me again. But flukes! man, what makes thee want to go a whaling, eh?—it looks a little suspicious, don't it, eh?— Hast not been a pirate, hast thou?—Didst not rob thy last Captain, didst thou?—Dost not think of murdering the officers when thou gettest to sea?"

I protested my innocence of these things. I saw that under the mask of these half humorous innuendoes, this old seaman, as an insulated Quakerish Nantucketer, was full of his insular prejudices, and rather distrustful of all aliens, unless they hailed from Cape Cod or the Vineyard.

"But what takes thee a-whaling? I want to know that before I think of shipping ye."

"Well, sir, I want to see what whaling is. I want to see the world."

"Want to see what whaling is, eh? Have ye clapped eye on Captain Ahab?"

"Who is Captain Ahab, sir?"

"Aye, aye, I thought so. Captain Ahab is the Captain of this ship."

"I am mistaken then. I thought I was speaking to the Captain him-self."

"Thou art speaking to Captain Peleg—that's who ye are speaking to, young man. It belongs to me and Captain Bildad to see the Pe-quod fitted out for the voyage, and supplied with all her needs, including crew. We are part owners and agents. But as I was going to say, if thou wantest to know what whaling is, as thou tellest ye do, I can put ye in a way of finding it out before ye bind yourself to it, past backing out. Clap eye on Captain Ahab, young man, and thou wilt find that he has only one leg."

"What do you mean, sir? Was the other one lost by a whale?"

"Lost by a whale! Young man, come nearer to me: it was devoured, chewed up, crunched by the monstrousest parmacetty that ever chipped a boat! —ah, ah!"

I was a little alarmed by his energy, perhaps also a little touched at the hearty grief in his concluding exclamation, but said as calmly as I could, "What you say is no doubt true enough, sir; but how could I know there was any peculiar ferocity in that particular whale, though indeed I might have inferred as much from the simple fact of the accident."

"Look ye now, young man, thy lungs are a sort of soft, d'ye see; thou dost not talk shark a bit. Sure ye've been to sea before now; sure of that?"

"Sir," said I, "I thought I told you that I had been four voyages in the merchant—"

"Hard down out of that! Mind what I said about the marchant service—don't aggravate me—I won't have it. But let us understand each other. I have given thee a hint about what whaling is; do ye yet feel inclined for it?"

"I do, sir."

"Very good. Now, art thou the man to pitch a harpoon down a live whale's throat, and then jump after it? Answer, quick!"

"I am, sir, if it should be positively indispensable to do so; not to be got rid of, that is; which I don't take to be the fact."

Seeing me determined, he expressed his willingness to ship me.

"And thou mayest as well sign the papers right off," he added—" come along with ye." And so saying, he led the way below deck into the cabin.

Seated on the transom was what seemed to me a most uncommon and surprising figure. It turned out to be Captain Bildad, who along with Captain Peleg was one of the largest owners of the vessel.

Now, Bildad, like Peleg, and indeed many other Nantucketers, was a Quaker, the island having been originally settled by that sect; and to this day its inhabitants in general retain in

54

an uncommon measure the peculiarities of the Quaker, only variously and anomalously modified by things altogether alien and heterogeneous. For some of these same Quakers are the most sanguinary of all sailors and whale-hunters. They are fighting Quakers; they are Quakers with a vengeance.

Like Captain Peleg, Captain Bildad was a well-to-do, retired whale-man. But unlike Captain Peleg, Captain Bildad had not only been originally educated according to the strictest sect of Nantucket Quakerism, but all his subsequent ocean life, and the sight of many unclad, lovely island creatures, round the Horn—all that had not moved this native born Quaker one single jot, had not so much as altered one angle of his vest. Still, for all this immutableness, was there some lack of common consistency about worthy Captain Peleg. Though refusing, from conscientious scruples, to bear arms against land invaders, yet himself had illimitably invaded the Atlantic and Pacific; and though a sworn foe to human bloodshed, yet had he in his straight-bodied coat, spilled tons upon tons of levia-than gore.

Such, then, was the person that I saw seated on the transom when I followed Captain Peleg down into the cabin.

"He says he's our man, Bildad," said Peleg, "he wants to ship."

"Dost thee?" said Bildad, in a hollow tone, and turning round to me.

"I dost," said I unconsciously, he was so intense a Quaker.

"What do ye think of him, Bildad?" said Peleg.

"He'll do," said Bildad, eyeing me, and then went on spelling away at his book in a mumbling tone quite audible.

"That's he; thank ye, Bildad. Now then, my young man, Ishmael's thy name, didn't ye say? Well then, down ye go here, Ishmael, for the three hundredth part of the ship's profits, if there should so chance to be any."

"Captain Peleg," said I, "I have a friend with me who wants to ship too—shall I bring him down to-morrow?"

"To be sure," said Peleg. "Fetch him along, and we'll look at him. Has he ever whaled it any?"

"Killed more whales than I can count, Captain Peleg."

"Well, bring him along then."

And, after signing the papers, off I went; nothing doubting but that I had done a good morning's work.

Next day, as we were walking down the end of the wharf towards the ship, Queequeg carrying his harpoon, Captain Peleg in his gruff voice loudly hailed us from his wigwam, saying he had not suspected my friend was a cannibal, and furthermore announcing that he let no cannibals on board that craft, unless they might prove their conversion to a Christian church.

Finding myself thus hard pushed, I replied. "Sir, he belongs to the same ancient Catholic Church to which you and I, and Captain Peleg there, and Queequeg here, and all of us, and every mother's son and soul of us belong; the great and everlasting First Congregation of this whole worshipping world; we all belong to that; only some of us cherish some queer crotchets no ways touching the grand belief; in THAT we all join hands."

"Splice, thou mean'st SPLICE hands," cried Peleg, drawing nearer. "Young man, you'd better ship for a missionary, instead of a fore-mast hand; I never heard a better sermon. Deacon Deuterono-my—why Father Mapple himself couldn't beat it, and he's reckoned something. Come aboard, come aboard; never mind about the papers. I say, tell Quohog there—what's that you call him? tell Quohog to step along. By the great anchor, what a harpoon he's got there! looks like good stuff that; and he handles it about right. I say, Quohog, or whatever your name is, did you ever stand in the head of a whale-boat? did you ever strike a fish?"

Without saying a word, Queequeg, in his wild sort of way, jumped upon the bulwarks, from thence into the bows of one of the whale-boats hanging to the side; and then bracing his left knee, and poising his harpoon, cried out in some such way as this: —

"Cap'ain, you see him small drop tar on water dere? You see him? well, spose him one whale eye, well, den!" and taking sharp aim at it, he darted the iron right over old Bildad's broad brim, clean across the ship's decks, and struck the glistening tar spot out of sight.

"Now," said Queequeg, quietly hauling in the line, "sposee him whale-e eye; why, dad whale dead."

"Quick, Bildad," said Peleg, "and get the ship's papers. We must have Hedgehog there, I mean Quohog, in one of our boats."

So down we went into the cabin, and to my great joy Queequeg was soon enrolled among the same ship's company to which I my-self belonged.

When all preliminaries were over and Peleg had got everything ready for signing, he turned to me and said, "I guess, Quohog there don't know how to write, does he? I say, Quohog, blast ye! dost thou sign thy name or make thy mark?"

But at this question, Queequeg, who had twice or thrice before taken part in similar ceremonies, looked no ways abashed; but taking the offered pen, copied upon the paper, in the proper place, an exact counterpart of a queer round figure which was tattooed upon his arm; so that through Captain Peleg's obstinate mistake touching his appellative, it stood something like this:—

Quohog.

his ∞ mark.

We embarked our few possessions and awaited the ship's departure. At length, towards noon of the following day, which chanced to be the twenty-fifth day of December, upon the final dismissal of the ship's riggers, and after the Pequod had been hauled out from the wharf, the two Captains, Peleg and Bildad, issued from the cab-in, and turning to the chief mate, Peleg said:

"Now, Mr. Starbuck, are you sure everything is right? Captain Ahab is all ready—just spoke to him—nothing more to be got from shore, eh? Well, call all hands, then. Muster 'em aft here—blast 'em!"

"No need of profane words, however great the hurry, Peleg," said Bildad, "but away with thee, friend Starbuck, and do our bidding."

How now! Here upon the very point of starting for the voyage, Captain Peleg and Captain Bildad were going it with a high hand on the quarter-deck, just as if they were to be joint-commanders at sea, as well as to all appearances in port. And, as for Captain Ahab, no sign of him was yet to be seen; only, they said he was in the cabin. But then, the idea was, that his presence was by no means necessary in getting the ship under weigh, and steering her well out to sea. Indeed, as that was not at all his proper business, but the pi-lot's; and as he was not yet completely recovered—so they said—therefore, Captain Ahab stayed below.

"Aft here, ye sons of bachelors," cried Peleg, as the sailors lingered at the main-mast. "Mr. Starbuck, drive'em aft."

Now in getting under weigh, the station generally occupied by the pilot is the forward part of the ship. And here stood Bildad, who, with Peleg, in addition to his other officers, was one of the licensed pilots of the port.

Meantime, overseeing the other part of the ship, Captain Peleg ripped and swore astern in the most frightful manner. I almost thought he would sink the ship before the anchor could be got up; involuntarily I paused on my handspike, and told Queequeg to do the same, thinking of the perils we both ran, in starting on the voy-age with such a devil for a pilot. I was comforting myself, however, with the thought that in pious Bildad might be found some salvation, spite of his seven hundred and seventy-seventh lay; when I felt a sudden sharp poke in my rear, and turning round, was horrified at the apparition of Captain Peleg in the act of withdrawing his leg from my immediate vicinity. That was my first kick.

"Is that the way they heave in the marchant service?" he roared. "Spring, thou sheep-head; spring, and break thy backbone!"

At last the anchor was up, the sails were set, and off we glided. It was a short, cold Christmas; and as the short northern day merged into night, we found ourselves almost broad upon the wintry ocean, whose freezing spray cased us in ice, as in polished armor.

At last we gained such an offing, that the two pilots were needed no longer. The stout sail-boat that had accompanied us began ranging alongside. Peleg turned to his comrade, with a final sort of look about him, —" Captain Bildad—come, old shipmate, we must go. Back the main-yard there! Boat ahoy! Stand by to come close alongside, now! Careful, careful! — come, Bildad, boy—say your last. Good-bye and good luck to ye all—and this day three years I'll have a hot supper smoking for ye in old Nantucket. Hurrah and away!"

"God bless ye, and have ye in His holy keeping, men," murmured old Bildad, almost incoherently. "I hope ye'll have fine weather now, so that Captain Ahab may soon be moving among ye. Good-bye, good-bye! Don't keep that cheese too long down in the hold, Mr. Starbuck; it'll spoil. Be careful with the butter—twenty cents the pound it was, and mind ye, if—"

"Come, come, Captain Bildad; stop palavering, —away!" and with that, Peleg hurried him over the side, and both dropt into the boat.

Ship and boat diverged; the cold, damp night breeze blew between; a screaming gull flew overhead; the two hulls wildly rolled; we gave three heavy-hearted cheers, and blindly plunged like fate into the lone Atlantic.

[2]

KNIGHTS AND SQUIRES

The chief mate of the Pequod was Starbuck, a native of Nantucket, and a Quaker by descent. He was a long, earnest man, and though born on an icy coast, seemed well adapted to endure hot latitudes, his flesh being hard as twice-baked biscuit. He was by no means ill-looking; quite the contrary. His pure tight skin was an excellent fit; and closely wrapped up in it, and embalmed with inner health and strength, like a revivified Egyptian, this Starbuck seemed prepared to endure for long ages to come, and to endure always, as now.

Yet, for all his hardy sobriety and fortitude, there were certain qualities in him which in some cases seemed well nigh to overbalance all the rest. Uncommonly conscientious for a seaman, and endued with a deep natural reverence, the wild watery loneliness of his life did therefore strongly incline him to superstition; but to that sort of superstition, which in some organizations seems rather to spring, somehow, from intelligence than from ignorance. Outward portents and inward presentiments were his. And if at times these things bent the welded iron of his soul, much more did his far-away domestic memories of his young Cape wife and child, tend to bend him still more from the original ruggedness of his nature, and open him still further to those latent influences which, in some honest-hearted men, restrain the gush of dare-devil daring, so often evinced by others in the more perilous vicissitudes of the fishery. "I will have no man in my boat," said Starbuck, "who is not afraid of a whale." By this, he seemed to mean, not only that the most reliable and useful courage was that which arises from the fair estimation of the encountered peril, but that an utterly fearless man is a far more dangerous comrade than a coward.

For, thought Starbuck, I am here in this critical ocean to kill whales for my living, and not to be killed by them for theirs; and that hundreds of men had been so killed Starbuck well knew. What doom was his own father's? Where, in the bottomless deeps, could he find the torn limbs of his brother?

Stubb was the second mate. He was a native of Cape Cod; and hence, according to local usage, was called a Cape-Cod-man. A happy-go-lucky; neither craven nor valiant; taking perils as they came with an indifferent air; and while engaged in the most imminent crisis of the chase, toiling away, calm and collected as a journeyman joiner engaged for the year. Good-humored, easy, and careless, he presided over his whale-boat as if the most deadly encounter were but a dinner, and his crew all invited guests.

What, perhaps, with other things, made Stubb such an easy-going, unfearing man, what helped to bring about that almost impious good-humor of his; that thing must have been his pipe. For, like his nose, his short, black little pipe was one of the regular features of his face. You would almost as soon have expected him to turn out of his bunk without his nose as without his pipe. He kept a whole row of pipes there ready loaded, stuck in a rack, within easy reach of his hand; and, whenever he turned in, he smoked them all out in succession, lighting one from the other to the end of the chapter; then loading them again to be in readiness anew. For, when Stubb dressed, instead of first putting his legs into his trousers, he put his pipe into his mouth.

The third mate was Flask, a native of Tisbury, in Martha's Vine-yard. A short, stout, ruddy young fellow, very pugnacious concerning whales, who somehow seemed to think that the great leviathans had personally and hereditarily affronted him; and therefore it was a sort of point of honor with him, to destroy them whenever encountered. In his poor opinion, the wondrous whale was but a species of magnified mouse, or at least water-rat, requiring only a little circumvention and some small application of time and trouble in order to kill and boil. He followed these fish for the fun of it; and a three years' voyage round Cape Horn was only a jolly joke that lasted that length of time.

Now these three mates—Starbuck, Stubb, and Flask, were momentous men. They it was who by universal prescription commanded three of the Pequod's whale boats as headsmen. In that grand order of battle in which Captain Ahab would probably marshal his forces to descend on the whales, these three headsmen were as captains of companies.

And since in this famous fishery, each mate or headsman, like a Gothic Knight of old, is always accompanied by his boat-steerer or harpooner, who in certain conjunctures provides him with a fresh lance, when the former one has been badly twisted, or elbowed in the assault; and moreover, as there generally subsists between the two, a close intimacy and friendliness; it is therefore but meet, that in this place we set down who the Pequod's harpooners were, and to what headsman each of them belonged.

First of all was Queequeg, whom Starbuck, the chief mate, had selected for his squire. But Queequeg is already known.

Next was Tashtego, an unmixed Indian from Gay Head, the most westerly promontory of Martha's Vineyard, where there still exists the last remnant of a village of red men, which has long supplied the neighboring island of Nantucket with many of her most daring harpooners. To look at the tawny brawn of his lithe snaky limbs, you would almost have credited the superstitions of some of the earlier Puritans, and half-believed this wild Indian to be a son of the Prince of the Powers of the Air. Tashtego was Stubb the second mate's squire.

Third among the harpooners was Daggoo, a gigantic, coal-black negro-savage, with a lion-like tread. In his youth Daggoo had voluntarily shipped on board of a whaler, and had since retained all the barbaric virtues of his native African coast, and erect as a giraffe, moved about the decks in all the pomp of six feet five in his socks. Curious to tell, this imperial negro, Ahasuerus Daggoo, was the Squire of little Flask, who looked like a chess-man beside him.

For several days after leaving Nantucket, nothing above hatches was seen of Captain Ahab. The mates seemed to be the only commanders of the ship; only they sometimes issued from the cabin with orders so sudden and peremptory, that after all it was plain they but commanded vicariously.

Now, it being Christmas when the ship shot from out her harbor, for a space we had biting Polar weather, though all the time running away from it to the southward, gradually leaving that merci-less winter behind us. It was one of those less lowering, but still grey and gloomy enough mornings of the transition, when as I leveled my glance towards the taffrail, foreboding shivers ran over me. Reality outran apprehension; Captain Ahab stood upon his quarter-deck.

There seemed no sign of common bodily illness about him, nor of the recovery from any. He looked like a man cut away from the stake, when the fire has overrunningly wasted all the limbs without consuming them, or taking away one particle from their compacted aged robustness.

So powerfully did the whole grim aspect of Ahab affect me, that for the first few moments I hardly noted that not a little of this over-bearing grimness was owing to the barbaric white leg upon which he partly stood. It had previously come to me that this ivory leg had at sea been fashioned from the polished bone of the sperm whale's jaw. "Aye, he was dismasted off Japan," said the old Gay-Head Indian once; "but like his dismasted craft, he shipped another mast without coming home for it. He has a quiver of 'em."

I was struck with the singular posture he maintained. Upon each side of the Pequod's quarter deck, and pretty close to the mizzen shrouds, there was an auger hole, bored about half an inch or so, into the plank. His bone leg steadied in that hole; one arm elevated, and holding by a shroud; Captain Ahab stood erect, looking straight out beyond the ship's ever-pitching prow. There was an infinity of firmest fortitude, a determinate, unsurrenderable willfulness, in the fixed and fearless, forward dedication of that glance.

Ere long, from his first visit in the air, he withdrew into his cabin. But after that morning, he was every day visible to the crew; either standing in his pivot-hole, or seated upon an ivory stool he had; or heavily walking the deck. By and by, it came to pass, that he was almost continually in the air.

Some days elapsed, and ice and icebergs all astern, the Pequod now went rolling through the bright Quito spring, which, at sea, almost perpetually reigns on the threshold of the eternal August of the Tropic.

Almost every twenty-four hours, when the watches of the night were set, and the band on deck sentineled the slumbers of the band below, ere long the old man would emerge, gripping at the iron banister, to help his crippled way.

Ahab, my Captain, still moves before me in all his Nantucket grim-ness and shagginess; and in this episode touching Emperors and Kings, I must not conceal that I have only to do with a poor old whale-hunter like him; and, therefore, all outward majestical trap-pings and housings are denied me. Oh, Ahab! what shall be grand in thee, it must needs be plucked at from the skies, and dived for in the deep, and featured in the unbodied air!

[3]

THE QUARTER-DECK

One morning shortly after breakfast, Ahab, as was his wont, ascended the cabin-gangway to the deck. There most sea-captains usually walk at that hour, as country gentlemen, after the same meal, take a few turns in the garden.

Soon his steady, ivory stride was heard, as to and fro he paced his old rounds. So full of his thought was Ahab, that at every uniform turn that he made, now at the main-mast and now at the binnacle, you could almost see that thought turn in him as he turned, and pace in him as he paced; so completely possessing him, indeed, that it all but seemed the inward mould of every outer movement.

"D'ye mark him, Flask?" whispered Stubb; "the chick that's in him pecks the shell. 'Twill soon be out."

The hours wore on; —Ahab now shut up within his cabin; anon, pacing the deck, with the same intense bigotry of purpose in his aspect.

It drew near the close of day. Suddenly he came to a halt by the bulwarks, and inserting his bone leg into the auger-hole there, and with one hand grasping a shroud, he ordered Starbuck to send everybody aft.

"Sir!" said the mate, astonished at an order seldom or never given on ship-board except in some extraordinary case.

"Send everybody aft," repeated Ahab. "Mast-heads, there! come down!"

When the entire ship's company were assembled, Ahab started from his standpoint; and as though not a soul were nigh him resumed his heavy turns upon the deck. But this did not last long. Vehemently pausing, he cried: —

"What do ye do when ye see a whale, men?"

"Sing out for him!" was the impulsive rejoinder from a score of clubbed voices.

"Good!" cried Ahab, with a wild approval in his tones; observing the hearty animation into which his unexpected question had so magnetically thrown them.

"And what do ye next, men?"

"Lower away, and after him!"

"And what tune is it ye pull to, men?"

"A dead whale or a stove boat!"

"Look ye! d'ye see this Spanish ounce of gold?"—holding up a broad bright coin to the sun—"it is a sixteen dollar piece, men. D'ye see it? Mr. Starbuck, hand me yon top-maul."

Receiving the top-maul from Starbuck, he advanced towards the main-mast with the hammer uplifted in one hand, exhibiting the gold with the other, and with a high raised voice exclaiming: "Whosoever of ye raises me a white-headed whale with a wrinkled brow and a crooked jaw; whosoever of ye raises me that white-headed whale, with three holes punctured in his starboard fluke—look ye, whosoever of ye raises me that same white whale, he shall have this gold ounce, my boys!"

"Huzza! huzza!" cried the seamen, as with swinging tarpaulins they hailed the act of nailing the gold to the mast.

"It's a white whale, I say," resumed Ahab, as he threw down the topmaul: "a white whale. Skin your eyes for him, men; look sharp for white water; if ye see but a bubble, sing out."

All this while Tashtego, Daggoo, and Queequeg had looked on with even more intense interest and surprise than the rest, and at the mention of the wrinkled brow and crooked jaw they had started as if each was separately touched by some specific recollection.

"Captain Ahab," said Tashtego, "that white whale must be the same that some call Moby Dick."

"Captain Ahab," said Starbuck, who, with Stubb and Flask, had thus far been eyeing his superior with increasing surprise, but at last seemed struck with a thought which somewhat explained all the wonder. "Captain Ahab, I have heard of Moby Dick—but it was not Moby Dick that took off thy leg?"

"Who told thee that?" cried Ahab; then pausing, "Aye, Starbuck; aye, my hearties all round; it was Moby Dick that dismasted me; Moby Dick that brought me to this dead stump I stand on now. Aye, aye," he shouted with a terrific, loud, animal sob, like that of a heart-stricken moose; "Aye, aye! it was that accursed white whale that razed me; made a poor pegging lubber of me forever and a day!" Then tossing both arms, with measureless imprecations he shouted out: "Aye, aye! and I'll chase him round Good Hope, and round the Horn, and round the Norway Maelstrom, and round perdition's flames before I give him up. And this is what ye have shipped for, men! to chase that white whale on both sides of land, and over all sides of earth, till he spouts black blood and rolls fin out. What say ye, men, will ye splice hands on it, now? I think ye do look brave."

"Aye, aye!" shouted the harpooners and seamen, running closer to the excited old man: "A sharp eye for the white whale; a sharp lance for Moby Dick!"

"God bless ye," he seemed to half sob and half shout. "God bless ye, men. Steward! go draw the great measure of grog. But what's this long face about, Mr. Starbuck; wilt thou not chase the white whale? art not game for Moby Dick?"

"I am game for his crooked jaw, and for the jaws of Death too, Captain Ahab, if it fairly comes in the way of the business we follow; but I came here to hunt whales, not my commander's vengeance. How many barrels will thy vengeance yield thee even if thou gettest it, Captain Ahab? it will not fetch thee much in our Nantucket market."

"Nantucket market! Hoot! But come closer, Starbuck; thou requirest a little lower layer. If money's to be the measurer, man, and the accountants have computed their great counting-house the globe, by girdling it with guineas, one to every three parts of an inch; then, let me tell thee, that my vengeance will fetch a great premium HERE!" cried Ahab, striking his chest.

"Vengeance on a dumb brute!" cried Starbuck, "that simply smote thee from blindest instinct! Madness! To be enraged with a dumb thing, Captain Ahab, seems blasphemous."

"All visible objects, man, are but as pasteboard masks. But in each event—in the living act, the undoubted deed—there, some un-known but still reasoning thing puts forth the moldings of its features from behind the unreasoning mask. If man will strike, strike through the mask! How can the prisoner reach outside except by thrusting through the wall? To me, the white whale is that wall, shoved near to me. Sometimes I think there's naught beyond. But 'tis enough. He tasks me; he heaps me; I see in him outrageous strength, with an inscrutable malice sinewing it. That inscrutable thing is chiefly what I hate; and be the white whale agent, or be the white whale principal, I will wreak that hate upon him. Talk not to me of blasphemy, man; I'd strike the sun if it insulted me. But look ye, Starbuck. Look! The crew, man, the crew! Are they not one and all with Ahab, in this matter of the whale? See Stubb! he laughs! See yonder Chilian! he snorts to think of it. Stand up amid the general hurricane, thy one tost sapling cannot, Starbuck! And what is it? Reckon it. 'Tis but to help strike a fin; no wondrous feat for Star-buck. What is it more? From this one poor hunt, then, the best lance out of all Nantucket, surely, he will not hang back, when every foremast-hand has clutched a whetstone? Ah!"

"God keep me! —keep us all!" murmured Starbuck, lowly.

"Cut your seizings and draw the poles, ye harpooners!" cried Ahab, unhearing.

Silently obeying the order, the three harpooners now stood with the detached iron part of their harpoons, some three feet long, held, barbs up, before him.

"Stab me not with that keen steel! Cant them; cant them over! know ye not the goblet end? Turn up the socket! So, so; now, ye cup-bearers, advance. The irons! take them; hold them while I fill!" Taking the pewter of grog from the steward by his side, and slowly going from one officer to the other, Ahab brimmed the harpoon sockets with the fiery waters.

"Now, commend the murderous chalices! Bestow them, ye who are now made parties to this indissoluble league. Ha! Starbuck! but the deed is done! Yon ratifying sun now waits to sit upon it. Drink, ye harpooners! drink and swear, ye men that man the deathful whaleboat's bow—Death to Moby Dick! God hunt us all, if we do not hunt Moby Dick to his death!" The long, barbed steel goblets were lifted; and to cries and maledictions against the white whale, the spirits were simultaneously quaffed down with a hiss. Starbuck paled, and turned, and shivered. Finally, the replenished pewter went the rounds among the frantic crew; when, waving his free hand to them, they all dispersed; and Ahab retired within his cabin.

[4]

THE FIRST LOWERING

I, Ishmael, was one of that crew; my shouts had gone up with the rest; my oath had been welded with theirs; and stronger I shouted, and more did I hammer and clinch my oath, because of the dread in my soul. A wild, mystical, sympathetical feeling was in me; Ahab's quenchless feud seemed mine. With greedy ears I learned the his-tory of that murderous monster against whom I and all the others had taken our oaths of violence and revenge.

For some time past, though at intervals only, the unaccompanied, secluded White Whale had haunted those uncivilized seas mostly frequented by the Sperm Whale fishermen. But not all of them knew of his existence; only a few of them, comparatively, had knowingly seen him; while the number who as yet had actually and knowingly given battle to him, was small indeed.

Nor was it his unwonted magnitude, nor his remarkable hue, nor yet his deformed lower jaw, that so much invested the whale with natural terror, as that unexampled, intelligent malignity which, according to specific accounts, he had over and over again evinced in his assaults. More than all, his treacherous retreats struck more of dismay than perhaps aught else. For, when swimming before his exulting pursuers, with every apparent symptom of alarm, he had several times been known to turn around suddenly, and, bearing down upon them, either stave their boats to splinters, or drive them back in consternation to their ship.

Judge, then, to what pitches of inflamed, distracted fury the minds of his more desperate hunters were impelled, when amid the chips of chewed boats, and the sinking limbs of torn comrades, they swam out of the white curds of the whale's direful wrath into the serene, exasperating sunlight, that smiled on, as if at a birth or a bridal.

His three boats stove around him, and oars and men both whirling in the eddies; one captain, seizing the line-knife from his broken prow, had dashed at the whale, as an Arkansas duelist at his foe, blindly seeking with a six-inch blade to reach the fathom-deep life of the whale. That captain was Ahab. And then it was, that suddenly sweeping his sickle-shaped lower jaw beneath him, Moby Dick had reaped away Ahab's leg, as a mower a blade of grass in the field. Small reason was there to doubt, then, that ever since that almost fatal encounter, Ahab had cherished a wild vindictiveness against the whale, all the more fell for that in his frantic morbidness he at last came to identify with him, not only all his bodily woes, but all his intellectual and spiritual exasperations. The White Whale swam before him as the monomaniac incarnation of all those malicious agencies which some deep men feel eating in them, till they are left living on with half a heart and half a lung. He piled upon the whale's white hump the sum of all the general rage and hate felt by his whole race from Adam down; and then, as if his chest had been a mortar, he burst his hot heart's shell upon it.

It is not probable that this monomania in him took its instant rise at the precise time of his bodily dismemberment. Then, in darting at the monster, knife in hand, he had but given loose to a sudden, passionate, corporal animosity; and when he received the stroke that tore him, he probably but felt the agonizing bodily laceration, but nothing more. Yet, when by this collision forced to turn towards home, and for long months of days and weeks, Ahab and anguish lay stretched together in one hammock, rounding in mid winter that dreary, howling Patagonian Cape; then it was, that his torn body and gashed soul bled into one another; and so interfusing, made him mad. That it was only then, on the homeward voyage, after the encounter, that the final monomania seized him, seems all but certain from the fact that, at intervals during the passage, he was a raving lunatic; and, though unlimbed of a leg, yet such vital strength yet lurked in his Egyptian chest, and was moreover intensified by his delirium, that his mates were forced to lace him fast, even there, as he sailed, raving in his hammock. In a strait-jacket, he swung to the mad rockings of the gales. And, when running into more sufferable latitudes, the ship, with mild stun'sails spread, floated across the tranquil tropics, and, to all appearances, the old man's delirium seemed left behind him with the Cape Horn swells, and he came forth from his dark den into the blessed light and air; even then, when he bore that firm, collected front, however pale, and issued his calm orders once again; and his mates thanked God the direful madness was now gone; even then, Ahab, in his hidden self, raved on. Ahab's full lunacy subsided not, but deepeningly contracted; like the unabated Hudson, when that noble Northman flows narrowly, but unfathomably through the Highland gorge. But, as in his narrow-flowing monomania, not one jot of Ahab's broad madness had been left behind; so in that broad madness, not one jot of his great natural intellect had perished. If such a furious trope may stand, his special lunacy stormed his general sanity, and car-ried it, and turned all its concentrated cannon upon its own mad mark; so that far from having lost his strength, Ahab, to that one end, did now possess a thousand fold more potency than ever he had sanely brought to bear upon any one reasonable object.

Now, in his heart, Ahab had some glimpse of this, namely: all my means are sane, my motive and my object mad. Yet without power to kill, or change, or shun the fact; he likewise knew that to man-kind he did long dissemble; in some sort, did still. But that thing of his dissembling was only subject to his perceptibility, not to his will determinate. Nevertheless, so well did he succeed in that dissembling, that when with ivory leg he stepped ashore at last, no Nantucketer thought him otherwise than but naturally grieved, and that to the quick, with the terrible casualty which had overtaken him.

The report of his undeniable delirium at sea was likewise popularly ascribed to a kindred cause. And so too, all the added moodiness which always afterwards, to the very day of sailing in the Pequod on the present voyage, sat brooding on his brow. Nor is it so very unlikely, that far from distrusting his fitness for another whaling voyage, on account of such dark symptoms, the calculating people of that prudent isle were inclined to harbor the conceit, that for those very reasons he was all the better qualified and set on edge, for a pursuit so full of rage and wildness as the bloody hunt of whales. Gnawed within and scorched without, with the infixed, un-relenting fangs of some incurable idea; such an one, could he be found, would seem the very man to dart his iron and lift his lance against the most appalling of all brutes. Or, if for any reason thought to be corporeally incapacitated for that, yet such an one would seem superlatively competent to cheer and howl on his underlings to the attack.

Here, then, was this grey-headed, ungodly old man, chasing with curses a Job's whale round the world, at the head of a crew, too, chiefly made up of mongrel renegades, and castaways, and cannibals. How it was that they so aboundingly responded to the old man's ire—by what evil magic their souls were possessed, that at times his hate seemed almost theirs; the White Whale as much their insufferable foe as his; how all this came to be—what the White Whale was to them, or how to their unconscious understandings, also, in some dim, unsuspected way, he might have seemed the gliding great demon of the seas of life,—all this to explain, would be to dive deeper than Ishmael can go. The subterranean miner that works in us all, how can one tell whither leads his shaft by the ever shifting, muffled sound of his pick? Who does not feel the irresistible arm drag? What skiff in tow of a seventy-four can stand still? For one, I gave myself up to the abandonment of the time and the place; but while yet all a-rush to encounter the whale, could see naught in that brute but the deadliest ill.

Though, consumed with the hot fire of his purpose, Ahab in all his thoughts and actions ever had in view the ultimate capture of Moby Dick; though he seemed ready to sacrifice all mortal interests to that one passion; nevertheless it may have been that he was by nature and long habituation far too wedded to a fiery whaleman's ways, altogether to abandon the collateral prosecution of the voyage.

To accomplish his object Ahab must use tools; and of all tools used in the shadow of the moon, men are most apt to get out of order. Even the high lifted and chivalric Crusaders of old times were not content to traverse two thousand miles of land to fight for their holy harpooner, without committing burglaries, picking pockets, and gaining other pious perquisites by the way. I will not strip these men, thought Ahab, of all hopes of cash—aye, cash.

For these reasons then, Ahab plainly saw that he must still in a good degree continue true to the natural, nominal purpose of the Pe-quod's voyage; observe all customary usages; and not only that, but force himself to evince all his well-known passionate interest in the general pursuit of his profession.

Be all this as it may, his voice was now often heard hailing the three mast-heads and admonishing them to keep a bright look-out, and not omit reporting even a porpoise. This vigilance was not long without reward.

It was a cloudy, sultry afternoon; the seamen were lazily lounging about the decks, or vacantly gazing over into the lead-colored waters. Queequeg and I were mildly employed weaving what is called a sword-mat, for an additional lashing to our boat.

Thus, we were weaving and weaving away when I started at a sound so strange, long drawn, and musically wild and unearthly, that the ball of free will dropped from my hand, and I stood gazing up at the clouds whence that voice dropped like a wing. High aloft in the cross-trees was that mad Gay-Header, Tashtego. His body was reaching eagerly forward, his hand stretched out like a wand, and at brief sudden intervals he continued his cries.

"There she blows! There! There! There! She blows! She blows!"

"Where-away?"

"On the lee-beam, about two miles off! A school of them!"

Instantly all was commotion.

The Sperm Whale blows as a clock ticks, with the same undeviating and reliable uniformity. And thereby whalemen distinguish this fish from other tribes of his genus.

"There go flukes!" was now the cry from Tashtego; and the whales disappeared.

The sailors at the fore and mizzen had come down; the line tubs were fixed in their places; the cranes were thrust out; the mainyard was backed, and the three boats swung over the sea like three samphire baskets over high cliffs. Outside of the bulwarks their eager crews with one hand clung to the rail, while one foot was expectantly poised on the gunwale. So look the long line of man-of-war's men about to throw themselves on board an enemy's ship.

But at this critical instant a sudden exclamation was heard that took every eye from the whale. With a start all glared at dark Ahab, who was surrounded by five dusky phantoms that seemed fresh formed out of air.

The phantoms, for so they then seemed, were flitting on the other side of the deck, and, with a noiseless celerity, were casting loose the tackles and bands of the boat which swung there. This boat had always been deemed one of the spare boats, though technically called the captain's, on account of its hanging from the starboard quarter. The figure that now stood by its bows was tall and swart, with one white tooth evilly protruding from its steel-like lips. A rumpled Chinese jacket of black cotton funereally invested him, with wide black trousers of the same dark stuff. But strangely crowning this ebonness was a glistening white plaited turban, the living hair braided and coiled round and round upon his head. Less swart in aspect, the companions of this figure were of that vivid, tiger-yellow complexion peculiar to some of the aboriginal natives of the Manillas;—a race notorious for a certain diabolism of subtle-ty, and by some honest white mariners supposed to be the paid spies and secret confidential agents on the water of the devil, their lord, whose counting-room they suppose to be elsewhere.

While yet the wondering ship's company were gazing upon these strangers, Ahab cried out to the white-turbaned old man at their head, "All ready there, Fedallah?"

"Ready," was the half-hissed reply.

"Lower away then; d'ye hear?" shouting across the deck. "Lower away there, I say."

Such was the thunder of his voice, that spite of their amazement the men sprang over the rail; with a wallow, the three boats dropped into the sea; while the sailors, goat-like, leaped down the rolling ship's side into the tossed boats below.

Hardly had they pulled out from under the ship's lee, when a fourth keel, coming from the windward side, pulled round under the stern, and showed the five strangers rowing Ahab, who, standing erect in the stern, loudly hailed Starbuck, Stubb, and Flask, to spread themselves widely, so as to cover a large expanse of water

"Pull, pull, my fine hearts-alive; pull, my children; pull, my little ones," drawlingly and soothingly sighed Stubb to his crew, some of whom still showed signs of uneasiness. "Why don't you break your backbones, my boys? The devil fetch ye, ye ragamuffin rapscallions; ye are all asleep. Stop snoring, ye sleepers, and pull. Why in the name of gudgeons and ginger-cakes don't ye pull? —pull and break something! Pull, and start your eyes out! Here!" whipping out the sharp knife from his girdle; "every mother's son of ye draw his knife, and pull with the blade between his teeth. That's it—that's it."

In obedience to a sign from Ahab, Starbuck was now pulling obliquely across Stubb's bow; and when for a minute or so the two boats were pretty near to each other, Stubb hailed the mate.

"Mr. Starbuck! Larboard boat there, ahoy! A word with ye, sir, if ye please!"

"Halloa!" returned Starbuck, turning round not a single inch as he spoke.

"What think ye of those yellow boys, sir!

"Smuggled on board, somehow, before the ship sailed. (Strong, strong, boys!)" in a whisper to his crew, then speaking out loud again: "A sad business, Mr. Stubb! (seethe her, seethe her, my lads!) but never mind, Mr. Stubb, all for the best. There's hogs-heads of sperm ahead, Mr. Stubb, and that's what ye came for. (Pull, my boys!) Sperm, sperm's the play! This at least is duty; duty and profit hand in hand."

"Aye, aye, I thought as much," soliloquized Stubb, when the boats diverged.

Stubb then withdrew his pipe from his hatband, where he always wore it aslant like a feather. He loaded it, and rammed home the loading with his thumb-end; but hardly had he ignited his match across the rough sandpaper of his hand, when Tashtego, his harpooner, whose eyes had been setting to windward like two fixed stars, suddenly dropped like light from his erect attitude to his seat, crying out in a quick frenzy of hurry, "Down, down all, and give way!—there they are!"

All four boats were immediately in keen pursuit of one spot of troubled water and air. But it bade fair to outstrip them; it flew on and on, as a mass of interblending bubbles borne down a rapid stream from the hills.

Soon we were running through a suffusing wide veil of mist; neither ship nor boat to be seen.

"Give way, men," whispered Starbuck, drawing still further aft the sheet of his sail; "there is time to kill a fish yet before the squall comes. There's white water again! —close to! That's his hump. THERE, THERE, give it to him!" whispered Starbuck.

A short rushing sound leaped out of the boat; it was the darted iron of Queequeg. Then all in one welded commotion came an invisible push from astern, while forward the boat seemed striking on a ledge; the sail collapsed and exploded; a gush of scalding vapor shot up nearby; something rolled and tumbled like an earthquake beneath us. The whole crew were half suffocated as they were tossed helter-skelter into the white curdling cream of the squall. Squall, whale, and harpoon had all blended together; and the whale, merely grazed by the iron, escaped.

Though completely swamped, the boat was nearly unharmed. Swimming round it we picked up the floating oars, and lashing them across the gunwale, tumbled back to our places.

Wet, drenched through, and shivering cold, despairing of ship or boat, we lifted up our eyes as the dawn came on. We heard a faint creaking, as of ropes and yards hitherto muffled by the storm. The sound came nearer and nearer; the thick mists were dimly parted by a huge, vague form. Affrighted, we all sprang into the sea as the Pequod at last loomed into view, bearing right down upon us within a distance of not much more than its length.

Floating on the waves we saw the abandoned boat, as for one instant it tossed and gaped beneath the ship's bows like a chip at the base of a cataract; and then the vast hull rolled over it, and it was seen no more till it came up weltering astern. Again, we swam for it, were dashed against it by the seas, and were at last taken up and safely landed on board.

"Queequeg," said I, when they had dragged me, the last man, to the deck, and I was still shaking myself in my jacket to fling off the water; "Queequeg, my fine friend, does this sort of thing often happen?" Without much emotion, though soaked through just like me, he gave me to understand that such things did often happen.

While the subordinate phantoms of Ahab's special crew soon found their place among the crew, though still as it were somehow distinct from them, yet that hair-turbaned Fedallah remained a muffled mystery to the last. Whence he came in a mannerly world like this, by what sort of unaccountable tie he soon evinced himself to be linked with Ahab's peculiar fortunes; nay, so far as to have some sort of a half-hinted influence; Heaven knows, but it might have been even authority over him; all this none knew. But one cannot sustain an indifferent air concerning Fedallah. He was such a creature as civilized, domestic people in the temperate zone only see in their nightmares, and that but dimly.

[5]

THE SPHINX

Some few days after rounding the Cape of Good Hope, off the distant Crozetts, a good cruising ground for Right Whalemen, a sail loomed ahead, the Albatross by name. As she slowly drew nigh, from my lofty perch at the fore-mast-head, I had a good view of that sight so remarkable to a tyro in the far ocean fisheries—a whaler at sea, and long absent from home.

As if the waves had been fullers, this craft was bleached like the skeleton of a stranded walrus. All down her sides, this spectral appearance was traced with long channels of reddened rust, while all her spars and her rigging were like the thick branches of trees furred over with hoar-frost. Only her lower sails were set. A wild sight it was to see her long-bearded look-outs at those three mast-heads. They seemed clad in the skins of beasts, so torn and bepatched the raiment that had survived nearly four years of cruising. Standing in iron hoops nailed to the mast, they swayed and swung over a fathomless sea; and though, when the ship slowly glided close under our stern, we six men in the air came so nigh to each other that we might almost have leaped from the mast-heads of one ship to those of the other; yet, those forlorn-looking fisher-men, mildly eyeing us as they passed, said not one word to our own look-outs, while the quarter-deck hail was being heard from below.

"Ship ahoy! Have ye seen the White Whale?"

But as the strange captain, leaning over the pallid bulwarks, was in the act of putting his trumpet to his mouth, it somehow fell from his hand into the sea; and the wind now rising amain, he in vain strove to make himself heard without it. Meantime his ship was still increasing the distance between. But taking advantage of his wind-ward position, Ahab again seized his trumpet, and knowing by her aspect that the stranger vessel was a Nantucketer and shortly bound home, he loudly hailed—" Ahoy there! This is the Pequod, bound round the world! Tell them to address all future letters to the Pacific Ocean! and this time three years, if I am not at home, tell them to address them to—" But the ship was gone, and could not hope to hear his final words.

Round the world! There is much in that sound to inspire proud feelings; but whereto does all that circumnavigation conduct? Only through numberless perils to the very point whence we started, where those that we left behind secure, were all the time before us.

The next day was exceedingly still and sultry, and with nothing special to engage them, the Pequod's crew could hardly resist the spell of sleep induced by such a vacant sea. For this part of the Indian Ocean through which we then were voyaging is not what whale-men call a lively ground; that is, it affords fewer glimpses of porpoises, dolphins, flying-fish, and other vivacious denizens of more stirring waters, than those off the Rio de la Plata, or the in-shore ground off Peru.

It was my turn to stand at the foremast-head; and with my shoulders leaning against the slackened royal shrouds, to and fro I idly swayed in what seemed an enchanted air. No resolution could with-stand it; in that dreamy mood losing all consciousness, at last my soul went out of my body; though my body still continued to sway as a pendulum will, long after the power which first moved it is withdrawn.

Suddenly bubbles seemed bursting beneath my closed eyes; like vices my hands grasped the shrouds; some invisible, gracious agency preserved me; with a shock I came back to life. And lo! close under our lee, not forty fathoms off, a gigantic Sperm Whale lay rolling in the water like the capsized hull of a frigate, his broad, glossy back, of an Ethiopian hue, glistening in the sun's rays like a mirror. But lazily undulating in the trough of the sea, and ever and anon tranquilly spouting his vapory jet, the whale looked like a portly burgher smoking his pipe of a warm afternoon. But that pipe, poor whale, was thy last. As if struck by some enchanter's wand, the sleepy ship and every sleeper in it all at once started into wakefulness; and more than a score of voices from all parts of the vessel, simultaneously with the three notes from aloft, shouted forth the accustomed cry, as the great fish slowly and regularly spouted the sparkling brine into the air.

"There she blows!"

"Clear away the boats! Luff!" cried Ahab. And obeying his own or-der, he dashed the helm down before the helmsman could handle the spokes.

The sudden exclamations of the crew must have alarmed the whale; and ere the boats were down, majestically turning, he swam away to the leeward, but with such a steady tranquility, and making so few ripples as he swam, that thinking after all he might not as yet be alarmed, Ahab gave orders that not an oar should be used, and no man must speak but in whispers. So, seated like Ontario Indians on the gunwales of the boats, we swiftly but silently paddled along; the calm not admitting of the noiseless sails being set. Presently, as we thus glided in chase, the monster perpendicularly flitted his tail forty feet into the air, and then sank out of sight like a tower swallowed up.

"There go flukes!" was the cry, an announcement immediately followed by Stubb's producing his match and igniting his pipe, for now a respite was granted. After the full interval of his sounding had elapsed, the whale rose again, and being now in advance of the smoker's boat, and much nearer to it than to any of the others, Stubb counted upon the honor of the capture. It was obvious, now, that the whale had at length become aware of his pursuers. All silence of cautiousness was therefore no longer of use. Paddles were dropped, and oars came loudly into play. And still puffing at his pipe, Stubb cheered on his crew to the assault.

"Start her, start her, my men! Don't hurry yourselves; take plenty of time—but start her; start her like thunder-claps, that's all," cried Stubb, spluttering out the smoke as he spoke. "Start her, now; give 'em the long and strong stroke, Tashtego. Start her, Tash, my boy—start her, all; but keep cool, keep cool—cucumbers is the word—easy, easy—only start her like grim death and grinning devils, and raise the buried dead perpendicular out of their graves, boys—that's all. Start her!"

"Woo-hoo! Wa-hee!" screamed the Gay-Header in reply, raising some old war whoop to the skies; as every oarsman in the strained boat involuntarily bounced forward with the one tremendous leading stroke which the eager Indian gave.

But his wild screams were answered by others quite as wild. "Kee-hee! Kee-hee!" yelled Daggoo, straining forwards and backwards on his seat, like a pacing tiger in his cage.

"Ka-la! Koo-loo!" howled Queequeg, as if smacking his lips over a mouthful of Grenadier's steak. And thus, with oars and yells the keels cut the sea. Meanwhile, Stubb retaining his place in the van, still encouraged his men to the onset, all the while puffing the smoke from his mouth. Like desperadoes they tugged and they strained, till the welcome cry was heard—" Stand up, Tashtego! —give it to him!" The harpoon was hurled. "Stern all!" The oarsmen backed water; the same moment something went hot and hissing along every one of their wrists. It was the magical line. An instant before, Stubb had swiftly caught two additional turns with it round the loggerhead, whence, by reason of its increased rapid circlings, a hempen blue smoke now jetted up and mingled with the steady fumes from his pipe. As the line passed round and round the loggerhead; so also, just before reaching that point, it blisteringly passed through and through both of Stubb's hands, from which the hand-cloths, or squares of quilted canvas sometimes worn at these times, had accidentally dropped. It was like holding an enemy's sharp two-edged sword by the blade, and that enemy all the time striving to wrest it out of your clutch.

"Wet the line! wet the line!" cried Stubb to the tub oarsman (him seated by the tub) who, snatching off his hat, dashed sea-water into it. More turns were taken, so that the line began holding its place. The boat now flew through the boiling water like a shark all fins. Stubb and Tashtego here changed places—stem for stern—a staggering business truly in that rocking commotion.

From the vibrating line extending the entire length of the upper part of the boat, and from its now being more tight than a harp-string, you would have thought the craft had two keels—one cleaving the water, the other the air—as the boat churned on through both opposing elements at once. A continual cascade played at the bows; a ceaseless whirling eddy in her wake; and, at the slightest motion from within, even but of a little finger, the vibrating, cracking craft canted over her spasmodic gunwale into the sea. Thus, they rushed; each man with might and main clinging to his seat, to prevent being tossed to the foam; and the tall form of Tashtego at the steering oar crouching almost double, in order to bring down his center of gravity.

"Haul in—haul in!" cried Stubb to the bowsman! and, facing round towards the whale, all hands began pulling the boat up to him, while yet the boat was being towed on. Soon ranging up by his flank, Stubb, firmly planting his knee in the clumsy cleat, darted dart after dart into the flying fish.

The red tide now poured from all sides of the monster like brooks down a hill. His tormented body rolled not in brine but in blood, which bubbled and seethed for furlongs behind in their wake. The slanting sun playing upon this crimson pond in the sea, sent back its reflection into every face, so that they all glowed to each other like red men. And all the while, jet after jet of white smoke was agonizingly shot from the spiracle of the whale, and vehement puff after puff from the mouth of the excited headsman; as at every dart, hauling in upon his crooked lance, Stubb straightened it again and again, by a few rapid blows against the gunwale, then again and again sent it into the whale.

"Pull up—pull up!" he now cried to the bowsman, as the waning whale relaxed in his wrath. "Pull up! —close to!" and the boat ranged along the fish's flank. When reaching far over the bow, Stubb slowly churned his long sharp lance into the fish, and kept it there, carefully churning and churning, as if cautiously seeking to feel after some gold watch that the whale might have swallowed, and which he was fearful of breaking ere he could hook it out. But that gold watch he sought was the innermost life of the fish. And now it is struck; for, starting from his trance into that unspeakable thing called his "flurry," the monster horribly wallowed in his blood, overwrapped himself in impenetrable, mad, boiling spray, so that the imperiled craft, instantly dropping astern, had much ado blindly to struggle out from that frenzied twilight into the clear air of the day.

And now abating in his flurry, the whale once more rolled out into view; surging from side to side; spasmodically dilating and contract-ing his spout-hole, with sharp, cracking, agonized respirations. At last, gush after gush of clotted red gore, as if it had been the purple lees of red wine, shot into the frighted air; and falling back again, ran dripping down his motionless flanks into the sea. His heart had burst!

"He's dead, Mr. Stubb," said Daggoo.

"Yes; both pipes smoked out!" and withdrawing his own from his mouth, Stubb scattered the dead ashes over the water; and, for a moment, stood thoughtfully eyeing the vast corpse he had made.

The Pequod's whale being decapitated and the body stripped so that the blubber should be rendered for its oil, the head was hoisted against the ship's side—about half way out of the sea, so that it might yet in great part be buoyed up by its native element. And there with the strained craft steeply leaning over to it, by reason of the enormous downward drag from the lower mast-head, and every yard-arm on that side projecting like a crane over the waves; there, that blood-dripping head hung to the Pequod's waist like the giant Holofernes's from the girdle of Judith.

A short space elapsed, and up into this noiselessness came Ahab alone from his cabin. Taking a few turns on the quarter-deck, he paused to gaze over the side, then slowly getting into the main-chains he took Stubb's long spade—still remaining there after the whale's Decapitation—and striking it into the lower part of the half-suspended mass, placed its other end crutch-wise under one arm, and so stood leaning over with eyes attentively fixed on this head.

It was a black and hooded head; and hanging there in the midst of so intense a calm, it seemed the Sphynx's in the desert. "Speak, thou vast and venerable head," muttered Ahab, "which, though ungarnished with a beard, yet here and there lookest hoary with mosses; speak, mighty head, and tell us the secret thing that is in thee. Of all divers, thou hast dived the deepest. That head upon which the upper sun now gleams, has moved amid this world's foundations. Where unrecorded names and navies rust, and untold hopes and anchors rot; where in her murderous hold this frigate earth is ballasted with bones of millions of the drowned; there, in that awful water-land, there was thy most familiar home. Thou hast been where bell or diver never went; hast slept by many a sailor's side, where sleepless mothers would give their lives to lay them down. Thou saw'st the locked lovers when leaping from their flaming ship; heart to heart they sank beneath the exulting wave; true to each other, when heaven seemed false to them. Thou saw'st the murdered mate when tossed by pirates from the mid-night deck; for hours he fell into the deeper midnight of the insatiate maw; and his murderers still sailed on unharmed—while swift lightnings shivered the neighboring ship that would have borne a righteous husband to outstretched, longing arms. O head! thou hast seen enough to split the planets and make an infidel of Abraham, and not one syllable is thine!"

[6]

THE PEQUOD MEETS THE RACHEL

The long and narrow peninsula of Malacca, extending south-eastward from the territories of Burma, forms the most southerly point of all Asia. In a continuous line from that peninsula stretch the long islands of Sumatra, Java, Bali, and Timor; which, with many others, form a vast mole, or rampart, lengthwise connecting Asia with Australia, and dividing the long unbroken Indian ocean from the thickly studded oriental archipelagoes. This rampart is pierced by several sally-ports for the convenience of ships and whales; conspicuous among which are the straits of Sunda and Malacca. By the straits of Sunda, chiefly, vessels bound to China from the west, emerge into the China seas.

Those narrow straits of Sunda divide Sumatra from Java; and standing midway in that vast rampart of islands, buttressed by that bold green promontory, known to seamen as Java Head; they not a little correspond to the central gateway opening into some vast walled empire: and considering the inexhaustible wealth of spices, and silks, and jewels, and gold, and ivory, with which the thousand islands of that oriental sea are enriched, it seems a significant pro-vision of nature, that such treasures, by the very formation of the land, should at least bear the appearance, however ineffectual, of being guarded from the all-grasping western world. The shores of the Straits of Sunda are unsupplied with those domineering fortresses which guard the entrances to the Mediterranean, the Bal-tic, and the Propontis. Unlike the Danes, these Orientals do not demand the obsequious homage of lowered top-sails from the endless procession of ships before the wind, which for centuries past, by night and by day, have passed between the islands of Sumatra and Java, freighted with the costliest cargoes of the east.

With a fair, fresh wind, the Pequod was now drawing nigh to these straits; Ahab purposing to pass through them into the Javan sea, and thence, cruising northwards, over waters known to be frequented here and there by the Sperm Whale, sweep inshore by the Philippine Islands, and gain the far coast of Japan, in time for the great whaling season there. By these means, the circumnavigating Pequod would sweep almost all the known Sperm Whale cruising grounds of the world, previous to descending upon the Whaling Line in the Pacific; where Ahab, though everywhere else foiled in his pursuit, firmly counted upon giving battle to Moby Dick, in the sea he was most known to frequent; and at a season when he might most reasonably be presumed to be haunting it.

Now, as many Sperm Whales had been captured off the western coast of Java, in the near vicinity of the Straits of Sunda; indeed, as most of the ground, roundabout, was generally recognized by the fishermen as an excellent spot for cruising; therefore, as the Pequod gained more and more upon Java Head, the look-outs were repeatedly hailed, and admonished to keep wide awake. But though the green palmy cliffs of the land soon loomed on the star-board bow, and with delighted nostrils the fresh cinnamon was snuffed in the air, yet not a single jet was descried.

When gliding by the Bashee isles we emerged at last upon the great South Sea; were it not for other things, I could have greeted my dear Pacific with uncounted thanks, for now the long supplication of my youth was answered; that serene ocean rolled eastwards from me a thousand leagues of blue.

To any meditative Magian rover, this serene Pacific, once beheld, must ever after be the sea of his adoption. It rolls the midmost waters of the world, the Indian ocean and Atlantic being but its arms. The same waves wash the moles of the new-built Californian towns, but yesterday planted by the recentest race of men, and lave the faded but still gorgeous skirts of Asiatic lands, older than Abraham; while all between float milky-ways of coral isles, and low-lying, end-less, unknown Archipelagoes, and impenetrable Japans. Thus, this mysterious, divine Pacific zones the world's whole bulk about; makes all coasts one bay to it; seems the tide-beating heart of earth. Lifted by those eternal swells, you needs must own the seductive god, bowing your head to Pan.

The Pequod held on her path towards the Equator. Making so long a passage through such unfrequented waters, descrying no ships, and ere long, sideways impelled by unvarying trade winds, over waves monotonously mild; all these seemed the strange calm things preluding some riotous and desperate scene.

One fine sunny day, a large ship, the Rachel, was descried, bearing directly down upon the Pequod, all her spars thickly clustering with men. At the time the Pequod was making good speed through the water; but as the broad-winged windward stranger shot nigh to her, the boastful sails all fell together as blank bladders that are burst, and all life fled from the smitten hull.

"Hast seen the White Whale?"

"Aye, yesterday. Have ye seen a whale-boat adrift?"

Throttling his joy, Ahab negatively answered this unexpected question; and would then have fain boarded the stranger, when the stranger captain himself, having stopped his vessel's way, was seen descending her side. A few keen pulls, and his boat-hook soon clinched the Pequod's main-chains, and he sprang to the deck. Immediately he was recognized by Ahab for a Nantucketer he knew. But no formal salutation was exchanged.

"Where was he? —not killed! —not killed!" cried Ahab, closely advancing. "How was it?"

It seemed that somewhat late on the afternoon of the day previous, while three of the stranger's boats were engaged with a shoal of whales, which had led them some four or five miles from the ship; and while they were yet in swift chase to windward, the white hump and head of Moby Dick had suddenly loomed up out of the water, not very far to leeward; whereupon, the fourth rigged boat—a reserved one—had been instantly lowered in chase. After a keen sail before the wind, this fourth boat seemed to have succeeded in fastening. In the distance he saw the diminished dotted boat; and then a swift gleam of bubbling white water; and after that nothing more; whence it was concluded that the stricken whale must have indefinitely run away with his pursuers, and since then not the least glimpse of the missing keel had been seen.

The story told, the stranger Captain immediately went on to reveal his object in boarding the Pequod. He desired that ship to unite with his own in the search; by sailing over the sea some four or five miles apart, on parallel lines, and so sweeping a double horizon, as it were.

"My boy, my own son is among them. For God's sake—I beg, I conjure"—here exclaimed the stranger Captain to Ahab, who thus far had but icily received his petition. "I will not go till you say aye to me. You too have a boy, Captain Ahab, though but a child, and nestling safely at home now. Yes, you relent; I see it—run men, now and stand by to square in the yards!"

"Avast," cried Ahab—" touch not a rope-yarn"; then in a voice that prolongingly molded every word—" Captain Gardiner, I will not do it. Even now I lose time. Good-bye, good-bye."

Soon the two ships diverged their wakes; and long as the strange vessel was in view, you plainly saw, by her still halting course and winding, woeful way, that this ship that so wept with spray, still remained without comfort. She was Rachel, weeping for her children, because they were not.

[7]

THE CHASE

And now that at the proper time and place, after so long and wide a preliminary cruise, Ahab; now, that he found himself hard by the very latitude and longitude where his tormenting wound had been inflicted; now that a vessel had been spoken which on the very day preceding had actually encountered Moby Dick; now it was that there lurked a something in the old man's eyes, which it was hardly sufferable for feeble souls to see. As the unsetting polar star, which through the livelong, arctic, six months' night sustains its piercing, steady, central gaze; so Ahab's purpose now fixedly gleamed down upon the constant midnight of the gloomy crew. It domineered above them so, that all their bodings, doubts, misgivings, fears, were fain to hide beneath their souls, and not sprout forth a single spear or leaf.

Nor, at any time, by night or day could the mariners now step upon the deck, unless Ahab was before them; either standing in his pivot-hole, or pacing the planks, never sleeping, never descending to his quarters. The clothes that the night had wet, the next day's sun-shine dried upon him.

The intense Pequod sailed on; the rolling waves and days went by, and another ship, most miserably misnamed the Delight, was descried. As she drew nigh, all eyes were fixed upon her broad beams, called shears, which, in some whaling-ships, cross the quarter-deck at the height of eight or nine feet; serving to carry the spare, unrigged, or disabled boats.

Upon the stranger's shears were beheld the shattered, white ribs, and some few splintered planks, of what had once been a whale-boat; but you now saw through this wreck, as plainly as you see through the peeled, half-unhinged, and bleaching skeleton of a horse.

"Hast seen the White Whale?"

"Look!" replied the hollow-cheeked captain from his taffrail; and with his trumpet he pointed to the wreck.

"Hast killed him?"

"The harpoon is not yet forged that ever will do that," answered the other, sadly glancing upon a rounded hammock on the deck, whose gathered sides some noiseless sailors were busy in sewing together.

"Not forged!" and snatching his leveled iron from the crotch were it lay, Ahab held it out, exclaiming—" Look ye, Nantucketer; here in this hand I hold his death!"

"Then God keep thee, old man—see'st thou that"—pointing to the hammock—" I bury but one of five stout men, who were alive only yesterday; but were dead ere night. Only THAT one I bury; the rest were buried before they died; you sail upon their tomb." Then turning to his crew—" Are ye ready there? place the plank then on the rail, and lift the body; so, then—Oh! God"—advancing towards the hammock with uplifted hands—" may the resurrection and the life—"

"Brace forward! Up helm!" cried Ahab like lightning to his men.

But the suddenly started Pequod was not quick enough to escape the sound of the splash that the corpse soon made as it struck the sea.

The next was a clear steel-blue day. The firmaments of air and sea were hardly separable in that all-pervading azure; only, the pensive air was transparently pure and soft, with a woman's look, and the robust and man-like sea heaved with long, strong, lingering swells, as Samson's chest in his sleep.

That night, in the mid-watch, when the old man—as his wont at intervals—stepped forth from the scuttle in which he leaned, and went to his pivot-hole, he suddenly thrust out his face fiercely, snuffing up the sea air as a sagacious ship's dog will, in drawing nigh to some barbarous isle. He declared that a whale must be near. Ahab rapidly ordered the ship's course to be slightly altered, and the sail to be shortened.

The acute policy dictating these movements was sufficiently vindicated at daybreak.

"Man the mast-heads! Call all hands! T'gallant sails! —stunsails! alow and aloft, and on both sides!"

All sail being set, he now cast loose the life-line, reserved for swaying him to the main royal-mast head; and in a few moments they were hoisting him thither, when, while but two thirds of the way aloft, and while peering ahead through the horizontal vacancy be-tween the main-top-sail and top-gallant-sail, he raised a gull-like cry in the air. "There she blows! —there she blows! A hump like a snow-hill! It is Moby Dick!"

"And did none of ye see it before?" cried Ahab, hailing the perched men all around him.

"I saw him almost that same instant, sir, that Captain Ahab did, and I cried out," said Tashtego.

"Not the same instant; not the same—no, the doubloon is mine, Fate reserved the doubloon for me. I only; none of ye could have raised the White Whale first. There she blows! —there she blows! —there she blows! There again! —there again!" he cried. "Stand by three boats, Mr. Starbuck, remember, stay on board, and keep the ship. Helm there! Luff, luff a point! All ready the boats there? Lower me, Mr. Starbuck; lower, lower, —quick, quicker!" and he slid through the air to the deck. "Stand by the braces! Hard down the helm! —brace up! Shiver her! —shiver her! —So; well that! Boats, boats!"

Soon all the boats but Starbuck's were dropped; all the boat-sails set—all the paddles plying; with rippling swiftness, shooting to lee-ward; and Ahab heading the onset. A pale, death-glimmer lit up Fedallah's sunken eyes; a hideous motion gnawed his mouth.

At length the breathless hunter came so nigh his seemingly unsuspecting prey, that his entire dazzling hump was distinctly visible, sliding along the sea as if an isolated thing, and continually set in a revolving ring of finest, fleecy, greenish foam. He saw the vast, involved wrinkles of the slightly projecting head beyond. Before it, far out on the soft Turkish-rugged waters, went the glistening white shadow from his broad, milky forehead, a musical rippling playfully accompanying the shade; and behind, the blue waters inter-changeably flowed over into the moving valley of his steady wake; and on either hand bright bubbles arose and danced by his side.

A gentle joyousness—a mighty mildness of repose in swiftness, invested the gliding whale. Not the white bull Jupiter swimming away with ravished Europa clinging to his graceful horns; not Jove, not that great majesty Supreme! did surpass the glorified White Whale as he so divinely swam. But soon the fore part of him slowly rose from the water; the grand god revealed himself, sounded, and went out of sight.

With oars apeak, and paddles down, the sheets of their sails adrift, the three boats now stilly floated, awaiting Moby Dick's reappearance.

But suddenly as he peered down and down into its depths, he profoundly saw a white living spot no bigger than a white weasel, with wonderful celerity uprising, and magnifying as it rose, till it turned, and then there were plainly revealed two long crooked rows of white, glistening teeth, floating up from the undiscoverable bottom. It was Moby Dick's open mouth and scrolled jaw; his vast, shad-owed bulk still half blending with the blue of the sea. The glittering mouth yawned beneath the boat like an open-doored marble tomb; and giving one sidelong sweep with his steering oar, Ahab whirled the craft aside from this tremendous apparition. Then, calling upon Fedallah to change places with him, went forward to the bows, and seizing his harpoon, commanded his crew to grasp their oars and stand by to stern.

Now, by reason of this timely spinning round the boat upon its axis, its bow, by anticipation, was made to face the whale's head while yet under water. But as if perceiving this stratagem, Moby Dick, with that malicious intelligence ascribed to him, and heedless of the irons darted at him from every boat, so crossed and recrossed, and in a thousand ways entangled the slack of the three lines now fast to him, that they foreshortened, and, of themselves, warped the devoted boats towards the planted irons in him; though now for a moment the whale drew aside a little, as if to rally for a more tremendous charge. Seizing that opportunity, Ahab first paid out more line: and then was rapidly hauling and jerking in upon it again—hoping that way to disencumber it of some snarls—when lo! —a sight more savage than the embattled teeth of sharks!

Through and through; through every plank and each rib, it thrilled for an instant, the whale obliquely lying on his back, in the manner of a biting shark, slowly and feelingly taking its bows full within his mouth, so that the long, narrow, scrolled lower jaw curled high up into the open air, and one of the teeth caught in an oar-lock. The bluish pearl-white of the inside of the jaw was within six inches of Ahab's head, and reached higher than that. In this attitude the White Whale now shook the slight cedar as a mildly cruel cat her mouse.

And now, while both elastic gunwales were springing in and out, as the whale dallied with the doomed craft in this devilish way; and from his body being submerged beneath the boat, he could not be darted at from the bows, for the bows were almost inside of him, as it were; and while the other boats involuntarily paused, as before a quick crisis impossible to withstand, then it was that mono-maniac Ahab, furious with this tantalizing vicinity of his foe, which placed him all alive and helpless in the very jaws he hated; frenzied with all this, he seized the long bone with his naked hands, and wildly strove to wrench it from its gripe. As now he thus vainly strove, the jaw slipped from him; the frail gunwales bent in, collapsed, and snapped, as both jaws, like an enormous shears, sliding further aft, bit the craft completely in twain, and locked themselves fast again in the sea, midway between the two floating wrecks, and captain and crew spilled into the frothy sea.

Moby Dick swam swiftly round and round the wrecked crew; sideways churning the water in his vengeful wake, as if lashing himself up to still another and more deadly assault. The sight of the splintered boat seemed to madden him. Though the other boats, unharmed, still hovered hard by; still they dared not pull into the eddy to strike, lest that should be the signal for the instant destruction of the jeopardized castaways, Ahab and all; nor in that case could they themselves hope to escape.

Meantime, from the beginning all this had been descried from the ship's mast heads; and squaring her yards, she had borne down upon the scene; and was now so nigh, that Ahab in the water hailed her!—"Sail on the"—but that moment a breaking sea dashed on him from Moby Dick, and whelmed him for the time. But struggling out of it again, and chancing to rise on a towering crest, he shouted, —" Sail on the whale! —Drive him off!"

The Pequod's prows were pointed; and breaking up the charmed circle, she effectually parted the white whale from his victim. As he sullenly swam off, the boats flew to the rescue.

"Any missing men?" said Ahab, half way rising, as Stubb dragged him into his boat.

"The Parsee!" cried Stubb—" he must have been caught in—"

"The black vomit wrench thee! —find him—not gone—not gone!"

"Aye, sir," said Stubb—" caught among the tangles of your line—I thought I saw him dragging under."

"MY line! MY line? Gone? —gone? What means that little word? —What death-knell rings in it, that old Ahab shakes as if he were the belfry. The harpoon, too!   -toss over the litter there, —d'ye see it? blistered fool! this hand did dart it! —'tis in the fish! Quick! —all hands to the rigging of the boats, a pull on all the sheets! —helm there! steady, steady for your life! I'll ten times girdle the unmeasured globe; yea and dive straight through it, but I'll slay him yet! Hands off from me! The eternal sap runs up in Ahab's bones again! Set the sail; out oars; the helm!"

The boats now made for the ship, and were soon swayed up to their cranes—the two parts of the wrecked boat having been previously secured by her—and then hoisting everything to her side, and stacking her canvas high up, and sideways outstretching it with stun-sails, like the double-jointed wings of an albatross; the Pequod bore down in the leeward wake of Moby-Dick. At the well known, methodic intervals, the whale's glittering spout was regularly announced from the manned mast-heads; and when he would be reported as just gone down, Ahab would take the time, and then pacing the deck, binnacle-watch in hand, so soon as the last second of the allotted hour expired, his voice was heard.—"Whose is the doubloon now? D'ye see him?" and if the reply was, No, sir! straightway he commanded them to lift him to his perch. In this way the day wore on; Ahab, now aloft and motionless; anon, unrestingly pacing the planks.

"Helm there! keep her full before the wind!—Aloft! come down!—Mr. Stubb, send a fresh hand to the fore-mast head, and see it manned till morning."—Then advancing towards the doubloon in the main-mast—"Men, this gold is mine, for I earned it; but I shall let it abide here till the White Whale is dead; and then, whosoever of ye first raises him, upon the day he shall be killed, this gold is that man's; and if on that day I shall again raise him, then, ten times its sum shall be divided among all of ye! Away now! —the deck is thine, sir!"

And so saying, he placed himself half way within the scuttle, and slouching his hat, stood there till dawn, except when at intervals rousing himself to see how the night wore on.

The morning dawned fair and fresh, and once more the solitary night-man at the fore-mast-head was relieved by crowds of the daylight look-outs, who dotted every mast and almost every spar.

"D'ye see him?" cried Ahab; but the whale was not yet in sight.

"Nothing, sir."

"Nothing! I've oversailed him. Aye, he's chasing ME now; not I, HIM. Aye, aye, I have run him by last night. About! about! Come down, all of ye, but the regular look outs! Stand by to sway me up!" cried Ahab, advancing to the hempen basket. "We should meet him soon."

"Aye, aye, sir," and straightway Starbuck did Ahab's bidding, and once more Ahab swung on high.

A whole hour now passed; gold-beaten out to ages. Time itself now held long breaths with keen suspense. But at last, some three points off the weather bow, Ahab descried the spout again, and instantly from the three mast-heads three shrieks went up as if the tongues of fire had voiced it.

He gave the word; and still gazing round him, was steadily lowered through the cloven blue air to the deck.

In due time the boats were lowered; but as standing in his shallop's stern, Ahab just hovered upon the point of the descent, he waved to the mate, —who held one of the tackle-ropes on deck—and bade him pause.

"Starbuck!"

"Sir?"

"Some men die at ebb tide; some at low water; some at the full of the flood; —and I feel now like a billow that's all one crested comb, Starbuck. I am old; —shake hands with me, man."

Their hands met; their eyes fastened; Starbuck's tears the glue.

"Oh, my captain, my captain! —noble heart—go not—go not! —see, it's a brave man that weeps; how great the agony of the persuasion then!"

"Lower away!"—cried Ahab, tossing the mate's arm from him. "Stand by the crew!"

In an instant the boat was pulling round close under the stern.

The boats had not gone very far, when by a signal from the mast-heads—a downward pointed arm, Ahab knew that the whale had sounded; but intending to be near him at the next rising, he held on his way a little sideways from the vessel; the becharmed crew maintaining the profoundest silence, as the head-beat waves hammered and hammered against the opposing bow.

"Drive, drive in your nails, oh ye waves! to their uttermost heads drive them in! ye but strike a thing without a lid; and no coffin and no hearse can be mine: —and hemp only can kill me! Ha! ha!"

Suddenly the waters around them slowly swelled in broad circles; then quickly upheaved, as if sideways sliding from a submerged berg of ice, swiftly rising to the surface. A low rumbling sound was heard; a subterraneous hum; and then all held their breaths; as bedraggled with trailing ropes, and harpoons, and lances, a vast form shot lengthwise, but obliquely from the sea. Shrouded in a thin drooping veil of mist, it hovered for a moment in the rain-bowed air; and then fell swamping back into the deep. But while it yet remained aloft, a quick cry went among the men, for lashed round and round to the fish's back as it flew; pinioned in the turns upon turns in which, during the past night, the whale had reeled the involutions of the lines around him, the half torn body of the Parsee Fedallah was seen; his sable raiment frayed to shreds; his distended eyes turned full upon old Ahab.

"Give way!" cried Ahab to the oarsmen, and the boats darted for-ward to the attack; but maddened by yesterday's fresh irons that corroded in him, Moby Dick seemed combinedly possessed by all the angels that fell from heaven. The wide tiers of welded tendons overspreading his broad white forehead, beneath the transparent skin, looked knitted together; as head on, he came churning his tail among the boats; and once more flailed them apart; spilling out the irons and lances from the two mates' boats, and dashing in one side of the upper part of their bows, but leaving Ahab's almost without a scar.

Whether fagged by the two days' running chase; or whether it was some latent deceitfulness and malice in him: whichever was true, the White Whale's way now began to abate. And still as Ahab glided over the waves the unpitying sharks accompanied him; and so pertinaciously stuck to the boat; and so continually bit at the plying oars, that the blades became jagged and crunched, and left small splinters in the sea, at almost every dip.

"Heed them not! those teeth but give new rowlocks to your oars. Pull on! 'tis the better rest, the shark's jaw than the yielding water."

"But at every bite, sir, the thin blades grow smaller and smaller!"

"They will last long enough! pull on! —But who can tell"—he muttered—" whether these sharks swim to feast on the whale or on Ahab? —But pull on! Aye, all alive, now—we near him. The helm! take the helm! let me pass,"—and so saying two of the oarsmen helped him forward to the bows of the still flying boat.

At length as the craft was cast to one side, and ran ranging along with the White Whale's flank, he seemed strangely oblivious of its advance—as the whale sometimes will—and Ahab was fairly within the smoky mountain mist, which, thrown off from the whale's spout, curled round his great, Monadnock hump; he was even thus close to him; when, with body arched back, and both arms' length-wise high-lifted to the poise, he darted his fierce iron, and his far fiercer curse into the hated whale. As both steel and curse sank to the socket, as if sucked into a morass, Moby Dick sideways writhed; spasmodically rolled his nigh flank against the bow, and, without staving a hole in it, so suddenly canted the boat over, that had it not been for the elevated part of the gunwale to which he then clung, Ahab would once more have been tossed into the sea. As it was, three of the oarsmen—who foreknew not the precise instant of the dart, and were therefore unprepared for its effects—these were flung out; but so fell, that, in an instant two of them clutched the gunwale again, and rising to its level on a combing wave, hurled themselves bodily inboard again; the third man helplessly dropping astern, but still afloat and swimming.

Almost simultaneously, with a mighty volition of ungraduated, instantaneous swiftness, the White Whale darted through the weltering sea. But when Ahab cried out to the steersman to take new turns with the line, and hold it so; and commanded the crew to turn round on their seats, and tow the boat up to the mark; the moment the treacherous line felt that double strain and tug, it snapped in the empty air!

"What breaks in me? Some sinew cracks! —'tis whole again; oars! oars! Burst in upon him!"

Hearing the tremendous rush of the sea-crashing boat, the whale wheeled round to present his blank forehead at bay; but in that evolution, catching sight of the nearing black hull of the ship; seemingly seeing in it the source of all his persecutions; bethinking it—it may be—a larger and nobler foe; of a sudden, he bore down upon its advancing prow, smiting his jaws amid fiery showers of foam.

Ahab staggered; his hand smote his forehead. "I grow blind; hands! stretch out before me that I may yet grope my way. Is't night?"

"The whale! The ship!" cried the cringing oarsmen.

"Oars! oars! Slope downwards to thy depths, O sea, that ere it be forever too late, Ahab may slide this last, last time upon his mark! I see: the ship! the ship! Dash on, my men! Will ye not save my ship?"

But as the oarsmen violently forced their boat through the sledge-hammering seas, the before whale-smitten bow-ends of two planks burst through, and in an instant almost, the temporarily disabled boat lay nearly level with the waves; its half-wading, splashing crew, trying hard to stop the gap and bale out the pouring water.

Meantime, for that one beholding instant, Tashtego's mast-head hammer remained suspended in his hand; and the red flag, half-wrapping him as with a plaid, then streamed itself straight out from him, as his own forward-flowing heart; while Starbuck and Stubb, standing upon the bowsprit beneath, caught sight of the down-coming monster just as soon as he.

"The whale, the whale! Up helm, ye fools, the jaw! Is this the end of all my bursting prayers? all my life-long fidelities? Oh, Ahab, Ahab, lo, thy work. Steady! helmsman, steady. Nay, nay! Up helm again! He turns to meet us! Oh, his unappeasable brow drives on towards one, whose duty tells him he cannot depart. My God, stand by me now!"

"Stand not by me, but stand under me, whoever you are that will now help Stubb; for Stubb, too, sticks here. I grin at thee, thou grinning whale! I grin at thee, thou grinning whale! Look ye, sun, moon, and stars! I call ye assassins of as good a fellow as ever spouted up his ghost. For all that, I would yet ring glasses with ye, would ye but hand the cup! Oh, oh! oh, oh! thou grinning whale, but there'll be plenty of gulping soon! Why fly ye not, O Ahab! For me, off shoes and jacket to it; let Stubb die in his drawers! A most moldy and over salted death, though; —cherries! cherries! cherries! Oh, Flask, for one red cherry ere we die!"

"Cherries? I only wish that we were where they grow. Oh, Stubb, I hope my poor mother's drawn my part-pay ere this; if not, few coppers will now come to her, for the voyage is up."

From the ship's bows, nearly all the seamen now hung inactive; hammers, bits of plank, lances, and harpoons, mechanically retained in their hands, just as they had darted from their various employments; all their enchanted eyes intent upon the whale, which from side to side strangely vibrating his predestinating head, sent a broad band of overspreading semicircular foam before him as he rushed. Retribution, swift vengeance, eternal malice were in his whole aspect, and spite of all that mortal man could do, the solid white buttress of his forehead smote the ship's starboard bow, till men and timbers reeled. Some fell flat upon their faces. Like dislodged trucks, the heads of the harpooners aloft shook on their bull-like necks. Through the breach, they heard the waters pour, as mountain torrents down a flume.

"The ship! The hearse!" cried Ahab from the boat; "its wood could only be American!"

Diving beneath the settling ship, the whale ran quivering along its keel; but turning under water, swiftly shot to the surface again, far off the other bow, but within a few yards of Ahab's boat, where, for a time, he lay quiescent.

"I turn my body from the sun. What ho, Tashtego! let me hear thy hammer. Oh! ye three unsurrendered spires of mine; thou uncracked keel; and only god-bullied hull; thou firm deck, and haughty helm, and Pole-pointed prow, —death-glorious ship! must ye then perish, and without me? Am I cut off from the last fond pride of meanest shipwrecked captains? Oh, lonely death on lonely life! Towards thee I roll, thou all-destroying but unconquering whale; to the last I grapple with thee; from hell's heart I stab at thee; for hate's sake I spit my last breath at thee. Sink all coffins and all hearses to one common pool! and since neither can be mine, let me then tow to pieces, while still chasing thee, though tied to thee, thou damned whale! THUS, I give up the spear!"

The harpoon was darted; the stricken whale flew forward; with igniting velocity the line ran through the grooves; —ran foul. Ahab stooped to clear it; he did clear it; but the flying turn caught him round the neck, and voicelessly as Turkish mutes bowstring their victim, he was shot out of the boat, ere the crew knew he was gone. Next instant, the heavy eye-splice in the rope's final end flew out of the stark-empty tub, knocked down an oarsman, and smiting the sea, disappeared in its depths.

For an instant, the tranced boat's crew stood still; then turned. "The ship? Great God, where is the ship?" Soon they through dim, bewildering mediums saw her sidelong fading phantom, as in the gaseous Fata Morgana; only the uppermost masts out of water; while fixed by infatuation, or fidelity, or fate, to their once lofty perches, the pagan harpooners still maintained their sinking lookouts on the sea. And now, concentric circles seized the lone boat itself, and all its crew, and each floating oar, and every lance-pole, and spinning, animate and inanimate, all round and round in one vortex, carried the smallest chip of the Pequod out of sight.

But as the last whelmings intermixingly poured themselves over the sunken head of the Indian at the mainmast, leaving a few inches of the erect spar yet visible, together with long streaming yards of the flag, which calmly undulated, with ironical coincidings, over the destroying billows they almost touched;—at that instant, a red arm and a hammer hovered backwardly uplifted in the open air, in the act of nailing the flag faster and yet faster to the subsiding spar. A sky-hawk that tauntingly had followed the main-truck downwards from its natural home among the stars, pecking at the flag, and incommoding Tashtego there; this bird now chanced to intercept its broad fluttering wing between the hammer and the wood; and simultaneously feeling that ethereal thrill, the submerged savage beneath, in his death-gasp, kept his hammer frozen there; and so the bird of heaven, with archangelic shrieks, and his imperial beak thrust upwards, and his whole captive form folded in the flag of Ahab, went down with his ship, which, like Satan, would not sink to hell till she had dragged a living part of heaven along with her, and helmeted herself with it.

Now small fowls flew screaming over the yet yawning gulf; a sullen white surf beat against its steep sides; then all collapsed, and the great shroud of the sea rolled on as it rolled five thousand years ago.

[8]

EPILOGUE

"AND I ONLY AM ESCAPED ALONE TO TELL THEE" Job.

The drama's done. Why then here does any one step forth? —Because one did survive the wreck.

It so chanced, that after the Parsee's disappearance, I was he whom the Fates ordained to take the place of Ahab's bowsman, when that bowsman assumed the vacant post; the same, who, when on the last day the three men were tossed from out of the rocking boat, was dropped astern. So, floating on the margin of the ensuing scene, and in full sight of it, when the half-spent suction of the sunk ship reached me, I was then, but slowly, drawn towards the closing vortex. When I reached it, it had subsided to a creamy pool. Round and round, then, and ever contracting towards the button-like black bubble at the axis of that slowly wheeling circle, like another Ixion I did revolve. Till, gaining that vital center, the black bubble upward burst; and now, liberated by reason of its cunning spring, and, owing to its great buoyancy, rising with great force, the life-buoy shot lengthwise from the sea, fell over, and floated by my side. Buoyed up for almost one whole day and night, I floated on a soft and dirge like main. The unharming sharks, they glided by as if with padlocks on their mouths; the savage sea-hawks sailed with sheathed beaks. On the second day, a sail drew near, nearer, and picked me up at last. It was the devious-cruising Rachel, that in her retracing search after her missing children, only found another orphan.

ABOUT THE EDITOR

Scott La Counte is a librarian and writer. His first book, Queit, Please: Dispatches from a Public Librarian (Da Capo 2008) was the editor's choice for the Chicago Tribune and a Discovery title for the Los Angeles Times; in 2011, he published the YA book The N00b Warriors, which became a #1 Amazon bestseller; his most recent book is #OrganicJesus: Finding Your Way to an Unprocessed, GMO-Free Christianity (Kregel 2016).

He has written dozens of best-selling how-to guides on tech products.

You can connect with him at ScottDouglas.org.

CPSIA information can be obtained
at www.ICGtesting.com
Printed in the USA
BVHW011318011121
620453BV00015B/755